Headlines

POVERTY

Molly Potter

A & C Black • London

INDIVIDUALS ENGAGING IN SOCIETY — Citizenship Foundation

Published 2010 by A & C Black Publishers Limited
36 Soho Square, London W1D 3QY

www.acblack.com

ISBN 978-1-4081-1356-1

Copyright text © Molly Potter 2010
Copyright illustrations © Karen Donnelly 2010
Series consultant: Roy Honeybone
Editor: Helen Foster

The publishers are grateful for permission to reproduce the following:
p. 58 FAIRTRADE mark © FAIRTRADE, reproduced by permission of the FAIRTRADE
Foundation. Every effort has been made to trace copyright holders and obtain
their permission for use of copyright material. The publishers would be
pleased to rectify any error or omission in future editions.

A CIP catalogue record for this book is available from the British Library.

Printed and bound in Great Britain by Caligraving.

A & C Black uses paper produced with elemental chlorine-free pulp, harvested
from managed sustainable forests.

All the internet addresses given in this book were correct at the time of
going to press. The author and publishers regret any inconvenience caused if
addresses have changed or sites have ceased to exist, but can accept no
responsibility for such changes.

Contents

Foreword

The books in this *Headlines* series tackle a range of important issues about which children and young people often think, especially when they hit the news headlines. Education for citizenship, though still non-statutory, should be an important element of the primary curriculum because it aims to help young people make sense of their world and understand the part they can play in making it a better place to live.

The Crick Report, in recommending that citizenship should become statutory in secondary schools, also suggested that it was relevant to primary children in helping them develop a sense of social and moral responsibility, understand their rights and responsibilities and also become politically literate. Critics might suggest that such aims are inappropriate for primary children but this is not so. Children from an early age actively attempt to make sense of the world around them in terms of important political ideas including fairness, power relations, laws and rules, right and wrong and so on. All of these are key citizenship concepts which, at secondary level focus on more explicitly political structures, but about which primary pupils are already developing ideas. In offering opportunities to debate and discuss what is happening in the world around them, and in helping young people develop their own ideas and their own voice, schools fulfil an important aim of general education which is no less than to help young people become responsible citizens.

Recently, the Independent Enquiry into Primary Education led by Sir Jim Rose, recommended that citizenship education, or social understanding, should be woven into a humanities strand, with history and geography, in order to remedy an important gap in the education provision of primary children. History and geography are important social strands of learning but in themselves, do not sufficiently address issues relating to the contemporary social world. Nor does it provide a curriculum space in which children can learn directly about their own rights and responsibilities, and develop the skills to think critically and thoughtfully about matters relating to their own welfare and that of wider society. Citizenship education also develops the skills of argument and debate so important in developing independence of thought and the confidence to know what one thinks and to express that appropriately in public settings. All these skills are developing rapidly during the primary years and citizenship education makes an important contribution to this process and that of developing respect for the views of others.

At about the same time that the Rose Review recommended citizenship should become an established strand of the curriculum, an authoritative study of primary education, led by Professor Robin Alexander, also recommended that citizenship education should be regarded as an essential part of primary education. One of the reasons the Cambridge Primary Review made this recommendation was because of citizenship's ability to nurture ethical reasoning. Moral education is a very necessary part of the education of every person, and yet very little direct attention is given to how schools help children develop a sense of right and wrong and work out for themselves what they think about issues in the wider world. Some teachers recoil at the notion that schools can or should get involved in telling children what their moral code should be. However, this is to misunderstand the purpose of enabling children to think ethically. In this sense moral instruction is not the same as moral education. Moral education nurtures children's ability to understand why some things in society are unacceptable, whilst other things are regarded as good, or important. Not that there will be complete agreement on such matters but that is not its purpose. Our society accepts that citizens' private moral views may differ and that different ways of life are acceptable so long as they do not operate to the detriment of others. That is why there is an important set of public values, which schools should convey to their pupils in class and reinforce through the practices and values of the institution, which are based on equality, respect for all, human rights, democracy and justice.

Schools, especially primary schools, are vital sites of social learning, where children, perhaps for the first time in their lives, begin to come up against people of different values and beliefs, behaviours, ethnicities, faiths, languages, countries of origins and so on. The primary socialisation that occurs within the family needs to be supplemented by secondary socialisation in which children learn there are other kinds of relation beyond those based on kinship and affection. However sound the education children gain at home, there are still important lessons to learn about the wider world and how it works and schooling plays a vital role in this. Moreover this is reinforced by the experiential citizenship learning which comes from everyday practices of involvement in school life, including student voice activities which provide practical experiences of community involvement, often beyond the school gates at local and even national and international levels. When messages from the taught and the experienced curriculum reinforce each other, children can become alerted to wider horizons and empowered to want to make a difference whether individually or with others.

The value of the Headlines series

This series of books addresses a range of issues about which primary school children are already aware and which they need to be able to understand, at an appropriate level. They are not trying to put 'old heads on young shoulders' or depress the children with the world's burdens. That would be wrong and unjustified. But the problems of violence, prejudice, poverty and war are issues which children can find deeply puzzling and we, as teachers, should try to help them deepen their understanding of them. There are several reasons for this.

The first is that children are often recipients of distorted messages which arrive through the medium of media headlines or sensationalising journalism. They may also be recipients of very one-sided views within the restricted family circle, so they lack the wider picture and do not develop the capacity to find out and think things through for themselves. They should also develop a sense of their own agency and appreciation of the fact that society is very much shaped by the individuals who make it up.

The material that has gone into this series is a mixture of knowledge and skills-based work which helps children to make sense of the issues and develop their conceptual understanding but also to develop essential thinking and emotional skills. Most of the material in this series is controversial in some way, some more than others. Naturally some of these topics are more challenging than others in content and different classes, even within the same school and year group, will vary in their capacity to deal with them adequately. So judicious choices may need to be made about which topics to cover and to what depth. Some of this material is perfectly suitable for use with children in Key Stage 3, given the wide variation in ability and experience within any age cohort of children.

Having emphasised the importance of developing children's thinking and empathy skills through discussing controversial issues, it needs to be emphasised that teachers may struggle to handle discussions of topics where their own knowledge is limited. It is important to let children air their views and to listen to the views of others but the role of the teacher is important in guiding the understanding of the children to deeper levels, in correcting important misinformation, and in balancing discussions when certain viewpoints are not spontaneously offered. Furthermore, discussing a social issue is not the same as discussing a scientific topic or the weather – it requires mastery of particular key words and ideas and particular forms of thinking and the skilled citizenship teacher provides structured opportunities for children to encounter these new ideas and use them in practice through debate, in group work, in presentations and in personal writing. That is why each book in this series provides a sound up-to-date introduction to the topic which, it is hoped teachers will find useful as background reading before teaching any of the lessons.

The Rose Review recommended that the stated aims of the primary curriculum should be the same as those now in place for the secondary curriculum, namely that it should enable students to become successful learners, confident individuals and responsible citizens. This surely makes practical sense. It cannot be helpful for our primary and secondary curricula to have different purposes because so much of what takes place in secondary schooling relies on the sound foundations laid in the primary school. In my own experience, primary teachers fully subscribe to the idea that the schooling they offer should help children prepare to play an active role as citizens, as laid out section 2 of the current PSHE and citizenship framework. However, teachers and schools differ in the extent to which they believe that social understanding and skills should be explicitly nurtured through the primary curriculum. The authors of this series firmly believe in the duty of the school to encourage the development of primary aged students as citizens, with rights and developing responsibilities, with social interests and skills. This is not to prematurely thrust them into adulthood but to help them become more rounded individuals better able to relate to others and better able to negotiate and contribute to the very complex world they inhabit.

Don Rowe
Director, Curriculum Development and Resources
Citizenship Foundation

Citizenship Foundation

is an educational charity which encourages and enables individuals to engage effectively in their communities and in democratic society at large. It works for better citizenship education, more effective participation in public life and stronger communities. Through curriculum development and support, the Foundation has championed the development of citizenship education in both primary and secondary schools, including its award-winning primary resources website 'Go Givers'. For more information about the Citizenship Foundation go to www.citizenshipfoundation.org.uk

Introduction

In a world where there are enough resources for everyone if they were split more evenly, the issue of poverty is fundamentally about inequality: those that have and those that have not. This is true not only within any one country but also when nations are compared. That some individuals in some countries can live a life of extreme luxury while others struggle to feed themselves daily seems one of the most complex puzzles to solve. What is clear is that there is no quick and simple solution.

In defining poverty, both absolute and relative measures are used. Absolute poverty measures the number of people or households unable to obtain their basic human needs (for example, food, safe drinking water, sanitation, health, shelter and clothing). It is used primarily when comparing poverty among different countries. Relative poverty measures the extent to which people or households fall below a financial threshold that renders them unable to access the usual standards of living in their particular economy or society. It is this latter definition that the UK government tends to adopt when developing policies that aim to address poverty in the UK.

Poverty affects the lives of hundreds of millions of people worldwide and millions here in the UK. It is a prevalent problem that many children will be aware of either through media coverage or direct experience.

Worldwide poverty

Images of starving children periodically appear on our screens as the media select images that will grab the attention of the audience. However, these images portray an acute situation that does not make obvious the more chronic circumstance of 1 in 4 children worldwide not eating enough protein or calories over long periods of time. Malnourished children do not grow properly, are more vulnerable to illness, can suffer from reduced mental development and have a short life expectancy. According to Oxfam, the number of hungry people in the world stands at 967 million and around 24,000 people – enough people to fill a football stadium – die daily from hunger-related causes.

Even for many of those who can feed themselves adequately, poverty can still impact significantly on the quality of their lives. If people cannot take for granted a comfortable and safe place to live, nearby access to clean water (that does not cause illness), healthcare provision and education rather than enforced labour for their children, they are said to live in poverty.

Organisations exist that attempt to address the issue of world poverty – and with some success. However,

because the causes of poverty are many, diverse and complex, what works to provide relief in one country will not necessarily work in another. Some cited causes of poverty for individuals within a country include:

- Political factors – for example, dictatorships that allow exploitation, government policies that enhance inequality, an absence of any kind of welfare, a government that has economic policies that fail to lift the country out of poverty.
- World debt – countries have to spend money servicing a debt; money that could be used to relieve the poverty of its people.
- Conflict – for example, war can leave people homeless and unable to grow food.
- Migration – sometimes people move looking for a better life but end up being exploited because of their vulnerability.
- Illnesses such as AIDS – these can reduce the proportion of young working adults in a country and in turn reduce the capacity a country has to grow food. AIDS also leaves dependent orphans. This can significantly affect the economy of a country.
- Lack of opportunities to escape from poverty – for example, through attaining employment, through education.
- Environmental factors – these include natural disasters that can leave people homeless and unable to grow food, or deforestation, which leaves the soil unsuitable for growing crops.

This list highlights the fact that addressing worldwide poverty cannot take a 'one glove fits all' approach. Most organisations tackling poverty agree that, while short-term relief is completely appropriate for acute disasters, long-term relief is nearly always about helping countries or individuals within it to help themselves. Therefore, governments worldwide need to prioritise this issue if it is to ever be successfully addressed.

Poverty in the UK

Britain is one of the wealthiest countries in the world. However, inequality means that in 2006/7 about 13 million individuals (nearly a quarter of the population) were living at or below what the government has defined as the poverty threshold.

It is estimated that about 1 in 3 children in the UK live in poverty. Some children in the UK, therefore, not only have direct experiences of going without things that they see other children access (e.g. birthday celebrations, owning a bicycle, swimming, having friends round for tea), but they also experience other more far-reaching effects. Poverty can mean that a child's future opportunities become limited: they are less likely to achieve academically (regardless of natural ability) and are far more likely to experience ill health – both physically and mentally. For these reasons poverty does not just impact upon 'the poor', it affects the whole of society in a variety of ways.

To end child poverty in the UK a multi-pronged approach needs to be taken. The following are some of the areas that have been identified as needing more development:

- Better jobs – better paid, long-term employment with opportunities for progression
- Better childcare to enable parents to work
- Raising the aspirations of children and young people
- More affordable and social housing.

As with world poverty, the issue of helping people to exit from poverty in this country in the long term is about helping people to help themselves.

This book aims to help teachers:

- explore key issues on the topic of poverty and inequality to develop pupils' understanding
- provide pupils with an awareness of poverty and its impact in the UK.
- provide pupils with a basic understanding of world poverty

Important note:

Many schools in the UK have pupils living in poverty in attendance and within any class there will be pupils from more financially affluent backgrounds than others. In dealing with this topic, it is crucial therefore that teachers are sensitive to this fact. Case studies have been used throughout this book to explore these sensitive topics 'at a distance' and at no time would it be appropriate to ask pupils to disclose details about their individual circumstances.

Key issues

Section 1

- to investigate pupils' perceptions and understanding of poverty.
- to consider the different ways in which poverty is defined.
- to consider what our individual views of poverty might be and start to consider inequality.
- to know that a country's politics can impact on the individual poverty.
- to have a basic understanding of a welfare state.
- to raise pupils' awareness of the campaigns and charities that aim to combat poverty.

Section 2

- to consider relative wealth and poverty in the UK.
- to consider what it means to live in relative poverty in the UK (from a child's viewpoint).
- to consider how the media portrays people and the impact this has on our idea of normality and subsequently success.
- to understand borrowing and debt, and how this can lead to poverty.
- to understand how poverty could be tackled through decisions the government make but that it cannot be solved overnight.
- to consider the government's target of getting rid of child poverty by 2020, the progress it has made and opinions on how the target could be met.
- to consider aspirations
- to consider conflicting viewpoints about poverty in the UK.

Section 3

- to consider global inequality.
- to explore the different causes of global poverty and their effects, and to realise how complex this issue is, with no simple solution.
- to consider how lifestyles that might seem quite different from our own are not necessarily considered to be a life of poverty.
- to consider the impact of extreme poverty for some children in India, and to empathise with a street child.
- to consider what living in poverty on the African continent is like and how it compares to life in the UK.
- to consider how people living in poverty worldwide can be helped
- to consider how political will is needed to effectively address the issues of poverty.
- to consider Fairtrade, its impact and its relationship to the consumer.
- to consider what would need to happen to combat poverty.

The CD-ROM

The CD-ROM provides extra resources for some lessons, such as newspaper reports, case studies or extra background information for pupils or teachers on topics discussed. Where this applies, these extra resources are listed in the lesson plan, and can be found organised by lesson on the CD-ROM. It also contains the activity sheets in the book as both PDF and Microsoft Word files. This allows them to be displayed on an electronic whiteboard, or be tailored by teachers to respond to a current event or issue. For more information on system requirements, please see the inside front cover.

Understanding poverty and inequality

This section aims to help pupils understand poverty and inequality and some related topics.

Key questions

- What is poverty?
- How is poverty defined?
- What is inequality?
- What is a welfare state?
- What work is being done to combat poverty?

Because of the sensitive nature of this topic, the use of case studies and empathy exercises lend themselves readily to distancing techniques. These are used so that pupils can explore these issues without having to disclose their personal circumstances. It is recommended that a ground rule preventing anyone referring to an individual's home, or personal comments, is developed before embarking upon these activities.

Learning objectives of the activities

- to investigate pupils' perceptions and understanding of poverty.
- to consider the different ways in which poverty is defined.
- to consider what our individual views of poverty might be and start to consider inequality.
- to know that a country's politics can impact on the individual poverty.
- to have a basic understanding of a welfare state.
- to raise pupils' awareness of the campaigns and charities that aim to combat poverty.

Learning objectives from the non-statutory guidance for PSHE and Citizenship

Pupils should be taught:
1 a) to talk and write about their opinions, and explain their views, on issues that affect themselves and society
2 a) to research, discuss and debate topical issues, problems and events
2 e) to reflect on spiritual, moral, social, and cultural issues, using imagination to understand other people's experiences
2 h) to recognise the role of voluntary, community and pressure groups
2 j) that resources can be allocated in different ways and that these economic choices affect individuals, communities and the sustainability of the environment
4 b) to think about the lives of people living in other places and times, and people with different values and customs
4 e) to recognise and challenge stereotypes

SPEAKING AND LISTENING

Listening

Pupils should be taught to:

2a. identify the gist of an account or key points in a discussion and evaluate what they hear

2b. ask relevant questions to clarify, extend and follow up ideas

2e. respond to others appropriately, taking into account what they say

Group discussion and interaction

Pupils should be taught to:

3a. make contributions relevant to the topic and take turns in discussion

3c. qualify or justify what they think after listening to others' questions or accounts

READING

Understanding texts

Pupils should be taught to:

2a. use inference and deduction

Reading for information

Pupils should be taught to:

3a. scan texts to find information

3c. obtain specific information through detailed reading

3e. use organisational features and systems to find texts and information

Non-fiction and non-literary texts

Pupils should be taught to:

5g. engage with challenging and demanding subject matter.

Key Vocabulary

- poverty
- inequality
- basic human needs
- welfare
- sanitation
- stereotype
- tax

How do we think of poverty?

Type of activity:
Investigation

Learning objective:
to investigate pupils' perceptions and understanding of **poverty**.

What to do:

1 Ask pupils to imagine a 10-year-old child – male or female. Explain to pupils that this child lives in poverty. You might need to explain, in simple terms, that this means s/he is poor.

2 Give individual pupils some paper and ask them to draw the child. Ask pupils to make up the following details about this child and to write/draw them around their picture:
- Name of child
- Where s/he lives
- What shows us that s/he is living in poverty

Also ask pupils to write any words they think could describe what it means to live in poverty.

3 Ask pupils to share their ideas with a partner and identify which were similar and which were different.

4 Explore pupils' ideas using the following questions:
- Have you drawn a child: From the past or the present? In this country or from a different country?
- What other information have you made up about this child?
- Can you tell from their appearance whether someone lives in poverty?
- Where have you heard information about what it means to be poor/live in poverty?

5 Explain to pupils that we all hold **stereotypes** in our heads. Stereotypes are what first come into our minds when we consider any type of person (e.g. what comes into our minds when we think of a footballer – male, trendy, rich). These stereotypes are sometimes unhelpful as they can lead to us making assumptions about a person before we actually know them. Ask pupils what assumptions they have made about people living in poverty and challenge their ideas with examples that could prove their assumptions wrong. For example, the idea that poor people lived in the past can be challenged by the fact that there are many people in the world today who are lucky if they get one meal a day.

Key points:

- As with many things, people have preconceptions about people living in poverty. This activity will highlight any stereotypes the children have picked up. Some may draw starving children from overseas, some orphans (like Oliver Twist), some ragged characters from fairy tales and a few a realistic image of what it means to live in poverty in the UK today.
- Hopefully, as pupils develop a deeper understanding of poverty, their image of poverty will diversify and stereotypes will be challenged.

Support/extension:

- Pupils could search for media stories about poverty and see how it is portrayed.
- Pupils could be asked to repeat this activity after several activities exploring the issue of poverty, to see if their ideas have changed.

Defining poverty

Type of activity:
Discussion

Learning objective:
to consider the two different ways in which **poverty** is defined.

Resources:
Pupil activity sheet 1 'Defining poverty' (p16) and Pupil activity sheet 2 'Defining poverty. Questions for discussion' (p17); one of each per pair

1 Give pairs of pupils a copy of the sheet 'Defining poverty' (p16). Read through the definitions of poverty and spend some time discussing these, checking pupils' understanding. You could use the sheet 'Defining poverty. Questions for discussion' (p17) to do this:

1 What is **sanitation**? (getting rid of sewage, measures needed to maintain public health and prevent diseases caused by the spread of bacteria)

2 Do you think everyone in this class gets their **basic human needs**? (probably)

3 Would you consider anything else to be a basic human need? (clothes, warmth, safety)

4 Do you believe you have the right to basic human needs?

5 Could you imagine living on 60p a day if it had to buy all your food, clothes and anything else you needed? (It needs to be explained that 60p does go further in many countries around the world, but it is still far too little for a person to have a comfortable life.)

6 In this country, do you see lots of people going without food, shelter, clean water and medicine? (probably not)

7 Many millions of people around the world struggle to get these basic things. Do you think living in poverty is the same in every country? (No, it is relative. What is deemed 'poverty' in the UK might not be in some countries.)

8 Different families in this country have different amounts of money. This has always been true. When might not having lots of money be a real problem? (If a person has to go without basic things like clothes, or without things that they see others around them have as standard, like a washing machine; if not having enough money makes you feel like you cannot join in with what other people are doing, like having birthday celebrations; if your health suffers through, for example, poor diet or not being able to access medical care.)

> NB: this discussion (particularly question 8) needs to be handled carefully and with sensitivity to pupils' personal circumstances. Try to keep the discussion about theoretical families and prevent pupils volunteering personal information.

2 Next ask pupils to consider Fatima and Meera and discuss the questions. Fatima is an example of absolute poverty as she is not getting enough food and cannot afford medical care. Meera is an example of relative poverty because, if Meera were to live near to Fatima, she would be considered wealthy; she has enough to eat, can access medical care, has adequate shelter and so on.

Key points:

- Poverty is defined either in absolute or relative terms.
- Definitions of absolute poverty tend to be used when looking at worldwide poverty as they use a set income threshold that enables one country to be compared with another. Definitions A and B describe absolute poverty.
- Relative poverty is usually used to look at poverty within a country as it uses some measure of comparison to determine an average income threshold in that country below which a person would be considered to be living in poverty. Definitions C and D describe relative poverty.
- Although a person living in relative poverty in the UK would seem to live a comparatively wealthy life to many people from around the world, the impact of this relative poverty must not be underestimated. Social exclusion and poor health outcomes can be a result of relative poverty in this country.

- Less able pupils could be given just two (rather than four) definitions for poverty:

  A) Poverty means you don't get enough to remain healthy and survive.

  B) Poverty that means you cannot afford some things many other people take for granted (e.g. school trips, bicycles).

Pupils could consider Maslow's hierarchy of needs as illustrated here. This model shows how a person's basic needs (e.g. food, water) need to be met before s/he can move up to the second level and show concern for safety or health. The first four levels are seen as deficiencies levels – it is essential that these needs are fulfilled before a person can do higher level things such as learn or be creative. In other words, if you do not have your basic physical needs met, if you do not feel safe, if you do not feel loved or have self-esteem, you can not be expected to learn. Many people in the world struggle to have their basic needs met and therefore are not in a position to attain the higher needs on this model.

ACTIVITY 3

Type of activity:
Sorting

Learning objective:
to consider what our individual views of **poverty** might be and start to consider **inequality**.

Resources:
Pupil activity sheet 3 'What do we think relative poverty might be?' (p18); one per pupil and two different coloured pencils per pair

What do we think relative poverty might be?

What to do:

1 Give individual pupils a copy of the sheet, 'What do we think relative poverty might be?' (p18) and clarify what is meant by the two criteria:
- **basic needs:** things that you would consider essential to live
- **needed for a good quality of life:** things that you personally would consider essential to live a life that was pleasant.

2 Ask individual pupils to select their colours and follow the instructions on the sheet without looking at how others are completing the task.

3 Then ask pupils to compare and discuss their 'answers' in pairs.

4 Next, as a class, try to collate a list of things that the whole class would deem 'basic needs'. Most people would consider the following to be basic needs:

- enough food to eat
- shelter
- clean water
- being able to see a doctor and getting medical treatment

- to be free from harm
- a comfortable and safe place to sleep
- warmth
- clothes
- to be able to keep clean

Some people might add further to this list if people's human rights were also considered to be a basic need. Point out that there are millions of people around the world who do not have their basic needs met. Also, discuss how just having these needs met will not necessarily mean a person has a good quality of life. For example, a child could have all their basic needs met but still have no opportunities that would make their life interesting or help them to fulfil their potential.

5 Ask pupils to consider what they have chosen as 'needed for a good quality of life'. These choices will be more subjective. Ask pairs of pupils to agree upon a list of things that fulfil this criterion. As the discussion unfolds, the idea of what constitutes a 'good quality of life' will develop. This might be slightly different for different pupils.

6 To finish the discussion, ask pupils to consider whether they think it is fair or not that most people around the world do not have what we consider is essential for a good quality of life. Also discuss the idea that some people (e.g. nomadic tribes in Sudan) would consider their lives to be good quality despite not having vast material possessions.

Key points:

- Many people around the world struggle to meet their basic human needs.
- Poverty is relative. Most people make comparisons with those around them to gauge their relative quality of life. Many lives in the developed world are luxurious compared to people living in poverty around the world.
- The developed world generally perceives material wealth as an indicator of quality of life. However, some would argue that accruing vast wealth does not automatically make a person happy. What a person in the UK might consider essential for a good quality of life might not be considered essential for a good quality of life in many parts of the world. For example, 'entertainment' might mean TV, cinema and meals out, but for other cultures it might mean singing, dancing and participating in community activities.
- Some of the things listed on the sheet are human rights. Having these rights honoured can have far more impact on a person's quality of life than their material possessions. Unfortunately, poverty and lack of rights often go hand in hand.

Support/extension:

- Less able pupils might need to work in a group and consider each thing on the list one by one – supported by an adult if possible.
- Pupils could draw a representation of 'a quality life' displaying all that they feel is essential for one.

ACTIVITY 4

Two nations

Type of activity:
Discussion

Learning objective:
to know that a country's politics can impact on individual **poverty** and to have a basic understanding of a **welfare** state.

Resources:
Pupil activity sheet 4 'Two nations' (p19); one per pair

What to do:

1 Ask pupils:
- Have you heard of the word '**tax**'?
- What do you think 'tax' is?

Depending upon their answers continue questioning pupils:
- Who pays tax? (There are lots of different types of tax, so most of us pay tax of some sort. VAT is one type of tax that is a proportion of the cost of many things we buy. Everyone who earns over a certain amount of money each year pays income tax, etc.) For current information and figures visit http://www.hmrc.gov.uk/rates/it.htm
- Who gets all the tax that people pay? (the government – local and national)
- What does the government do with this money? (many things: e.g. pay for schools, build roads, pay for the health service, help out people on low incomes)

2 Explain to pupils that people pay more tax in some countries than others. High-tax-paying countries (e.g. Sweden) usually spend a lot on their 'welfare system' and these countries are described as being 'welfare states'. The welfare state looks after people, especially people on low incomes, and tries to ensure that everyone can get, for example, healthcare and education for, and that no one lives in absolute poverty. The UK has a welfare system.

3 Give pairs of pupils a copy of the sheet 'Two nations' (p19). Work through the text together and ask pupils to discuss questions 1 to 8 in pairs. Possible answers might be:
　　1 Probably Ayland because she would hand over less of her money in taxes.
　　2 Beeland because he would get benefits to prevent him living in poverty.

3 It would depend on whether he believed that paying taxes so that everyone in the country could live comfortably was a good idea or not.

4 Mr Smart because he might be happy to pay high taxes to support a welfare state or he might prefer to pay low taxes.

5 No – Ms Able might be happy to pay high taxes to help other people in her country. Mr Hardworking might assume he will one day get a well-paid job and not want to pay high taxes.

6 She might believe that it was wrong for the government to take so much of her money in tax.

7 He would probably be living in poverty.

8 Open to discussion.

4 Close the discussion by outlining some of the key points below to the whole class.

Key points:

- This activity illustrates that preventing poverty can cost a nation money – usually gained through tax payments – which some people can resent. Beeland is a welfare state.
- Historically, left wing politics (Beeland) maintained a welfare state through higher taxes than right wing politics (Ayland) that had lower taxes and did not prioritise the welfare state. Left wing politics favour people living in poverty and right wing politics financially favoured people on high incomes. Individuals vote for governments that make decisions they feel will benefit themselves the most or vote for those they believe have the best policies that will be of most benefit to the country they live in.
- Some people believe that if there are some people in a country earning lots of money, everyone in that country should/will benefit, but others believe it just widens the gap between high earners and those living in poverty.
- Many people, rich or poor, can see that poverty causes lots of problems (e.g. crime and ill health) and it is in everyone's interest that poverty is prevented.
- A government's policies can have a significant impact on its nation's poverty.
- Some governments prioritise preventing poverty more than others.

Support/extension:

- Take time to explain the different politics of Ayland and Beeland to less able pupils.
- Pupils could use the Internet to investigate which countries have a welfare state.

Charities and campaigns

Type of activity:
Investigation

Learning objective:
to raise pupils' awareness of the campaigns and charities that aim to combat **poverty.**

Resources:
Pupil activity sheet 5 'Charities and campaigns' (p20); one per pair: access to the Internet

What to do:

1 Give pairs of pupils the sheet 'Charities and campaigns' (p20). Ask them to investigate the four listed websites, which can be located by typing the charity/campaign name into any search engine.

2 Explain that although pupils have some specific things to investigate, you are happy for them to explore each website as much as they like. You could encourage this by asking pupils to find out as many facts about and examples of the effects of poverty as they can from all four websites.

3 Leave 10 minutes at the end of the session to lead a discussion about the information pupils have gathered. Questions might include:
- Were you aware of any of these charities/campaigns before today? If so, why or how?
- Did you discover anything that shocked you?
- How have different charities persuaded people to donate money?

- What is each website trying to do?
- Share something that you found out.

Key points:

- Oxfam, Save the Children and Children in Crisis are three of many charities that aim to combat world poverty and its related effects.
- End Child Poverty is a UK campaign that is supported by many different organisations and charities.

Support/extension:

- Pupils could make posters displaying the interesting facts about poverty and the charities/campaigns that they have found. There are additional websites listed in the back of this book that provide sources of information about poverty.
- More able pupils could summarise the work each charity/campaign does.
- Pupils could discuss and develop a fund-raising activity for one of the charities.
- Pupils could explore how some celebrities are affiliated to different charities and how this might help raise funds. They could also consider whether or not a person has a duty to support a charity if they are a rich celebrity.

Defining poverty

Poverty is quite difficult to describe and defining it is not simple. Here are some definitions that have been used.

A A person might be said to be living in poverty if they cannot get things that are considered to be basic human needs (for example: food, safe drinking water, sanitation, health and shelter).

B The world bank defines extreme poverty as living on less than USD $1 (about 60p) a day and moderate poverty as less than USD $2 a day.

C A person might be considered to be living in poverty if they cannot afford the things that most people in their country can afford. This means they do not have what is considered to be a good enough way of life for the country in which they live.

D A household is considered to be living in poverty if it has to live on an income that is less than 60% of the average household income.

Think about these two children. Both are considered to be living in poverty.

Fatima and her mother struggle to get enough food to eat every day. Because of lack of food, Fatima has become ill. Paying for medicine would mean they would both have to go without food.

Meera lives with her mum in a flat. They just about get by, but Meera is aware that she has to go without lots of things that she sees her friends having.

Discuss:

1 Which of these children do you think lives in the UK?

2 Look at the definitions of poverty. Which definition do you think would be used to describe Fatima's poverty and which do you think would be used to describe Meera's poverty?

Defining poverty
Questions for discussion

1 What is sanitation and why is it important?

2 Do you think everyone in this class gets their basic human needs?

3 Do you think anything else is a basic human need?

4 Do you believe you have the right to the basic human needs listed in definition A?

5 Could you imagine living on 60p a day if it had to buy all your food, clothes and anything else you needed?

6 In this country, do you see lots of people going without food, shelter, clean water and medicine?

7 Many millions of people around the world struggle to get these basic things. Do you think living in poverty is the same in every country?

8 Different families in this country have different amounts of money. This has always been true. When might not having lots of money be a real problem?

What do we think poverty might be?

In one colour circle which of the following you think are **basic needs** and in another colour, circle things that you think are **needed for a good quality of life**. You do not need to circle everything.

- enough food to eat

- plenty of food choices

- to be paid fairly for the work you do

- to feel loved

- to feel safe

- to be able to take part in the activities people around you are taking part in

- shelter

- running water to your home

- clean water

- to be able to see a doctor and get medical treatment

- to be free from harm

- to have injections for preventable diseases

- to learn to read

- an education that means you can make the most of yourself

- entertainment

- friends

- hot water

- to be able to buy presents for people you care about

- to be respected

- a holiday away from home once a year

- to be free to hold your own opinions (as long as they do not impact on the rights of others)

- to be treated fairly

- to be able to communicate with people who don't live nearby

- a comfortable and safe place to sleep

- warmth

- living to old age

- some time off from working

- to be able to discuss things

- to be able to make some decisions about issues that affect you

- to be able to choose how you work to earn money

- to be able to have fun

- not to have to work when you are a young child

- clothes

- to be able to travel

- a choice of clothes

- to be able to keep clean

- to be able to buy anything you want

Two nations

Ms Able is a businesswoman who owns and manages several extremely successful restaurants that make an incredible amount of money each year.

Mr Smart is a teacher and earns enough money to live comfortably.

Mr Hardworking is a gardener and if he had to live on just his earnings, he would struggle to feed and clothe himself.

Here are two different countries:

Ayland	Beeland
In Ayland, people pay very little of the money they earn in taxes. This means they get to keep nearly all of the money they earn.	In Beeland, people pay taxes once they earn over a certain amount of money. These taxes are paid to the government – which then decides how it is spent. It is spent on things like paying benefits (money to help people) to families that do not earn much money, and paying for hospitals and schools so that medical care and education are free.

Now discuss:

1 Which country do you think Ms Able would most like to live in? Why?

2 Which country do you think Mr Hardworking would most like to live in? Why?

3 Which country do you think Mr Smart would most like to live in? Why?

4 Which of these three people was it hardest to answer this question for? Why?

5 Could you be certain that these people would want to live in the country you chose for them?

6 If Ms Able lived in Beeland, what might she say about the taxes she had to pay?

7 If Mr Hardworking lived in Ayland, what would his life be like?

8 Which country do you think you would you most like to live in? Why?

Charities and campaigns

There are many organisations, charities and governments that are trying to get rid of poverty. Use the Internet to try and find out the following information about these charities or campaigns:

Oxfam   **Save the Children**   **Children in Crisis**   **End Child Poverty**

Oxfam	Children in Crisis
Does Oxfam work just in the UK or worldwide?	Name a country Children in Crisis are working in and what they are doing there.
A fact about hunger you found on the website:	What tool does Children in Crisis believe is needed to overcome poverty?
Name a way Oxfam suggests you can get involved:	Name a way Children in Crisis suggests you can get involved:
Save the Children	**End Child Poverty**
Does it work just in the UK or worldwide?	Does it work just in the UK or worldwide?
What is the Save the Children slogan?	How many organisations are part of this campaign?
Name a way Save the Children suggests you can get involved:	Name a way the End Child Poverty website suggests you can help:

SECTION 2

Poverty in the UK

This section aims to help pupils understand poverty and inequality issues in the UK.

Key questions

- How does living in poverty in the UK affect people?
- What is stigma and does poverty have stigmas associated with it?
- How does the media influence our idea of success?
- What is debt?
- What is the government trying to do about poverty in the UK and how successful is it?
- What are aspirations?
- What do people think about poverty in the UK?

Learning objectives of the activities

- to consider relative wealth and poverty in the UK.
- to consider what it means to live in relative poverty in the UK (from a child's viewpoint).
- to consider the stigma associated with poverty.
- to consider how the media portrays people and the impact this has on our idea of normality and subsequently success.
- to understand borrowing and debt, and how this can lead to poverty.
- to understand how poverty could be tackled through decisions the government make but that it cannot be solved overnight.
- to consider the government's target of getting rid of child poverty by 2020, the progress it has made and opinions on how the target could be met.
- to consider aspirations.
- to consider conflicting viewpoints about poverty in the UK.

Learning objectives from the non-statutory guidance for PSHE and Citizenship

Pupils should be taught:

1 a) to talk and write about their opinions, and explain their views, on issues that affect themselves and society

1 b) to recognise their worth as individuals by identifying positive things about themselves and their achievements, seeing their mistakes, making amends and setting personal goals

1 f) to look after their money and realise that future wants and needs may be met through saving

2 a) to research, discuss and debate topical issues, problems and events

2 e) to reflect on spiritual, moral, social, and cultural issues, using imagination to understand other people's experiences

2 j) that resources can be allocated in different ways and that these economic choices affect individuals, communities and the sustainability of the environment

2 k) to explore how the media present information

4 a) that their actions affect themselves and others, to care about other people's feelings and to try to see things from their points of view

SPEAKING AND LISTENING

Listening
Pupils should be taught to:

2a. identify the gist of an account or key points in a discussion and evaluate what they hear

2b. ask relevant questions to clarify, extend and follow up ideas

2e. respond to others appropriately, taking into account what they say

Group discussion and interaction
Pupils should be taught to:

3a. make contributions relevant to the topic and take turns in discussion

3c. qualify or justify what they think after listening to others' questions or accounts

READING

Understanding texts
Pupils should be taught to:

2a. use inference and deduction

2b. look for meaning beyond the literal

Reading for information
Pupils should be taught to:

3a. scan texts to find information

3b. skim for gist and overall impression

3c. obtain specific information through detailed reading

3g. consider an argument critically

Non-fiction and non-literary texts
Pupils should be taught to:

5g. engage with challenging and demanding subject matter.

WRITING

Composition
Pupils should be taught to:

1a. choose form and content to suit a particular purpose [for example, notes to read or organise thinking, plans for action, poetry for pleasure]

1c. use language and style that are appropriate to the reader

1e. use features of layout, presentation and organisation effectively

Planning and drafting
Pupils should be taught to:

2a. plan – note and develop initial ideas

2b. draft – develop ideas from the plan into structured written text

2c. revise – change and improve the draft

Key Vocabulary
- stigma
- success
- debt
- aspirations
- interest
- credit card
- empathy
- sympathy

ACTIVITY 1

Type of activity:
Discussion prompted by statements

Learning objective:
to consider the impact of relative wealth and poverty in the UK.

Resources:
Pupil activity sheet 6 'What do you think about poverty and wealth in the UK?' (p34); one per pupil

What do you think about poverty and wealth in the UK?

What to do:

1 Give pairs of pupils a copy of the sheet 'What do you think about poverty and wealth in the UK?' (p34). Ask individual pupils to consider how much they agree or disagree with each of the statements on the sheet.

2 Then ask pupils to discuss their viewpoints in pairs.

3 Finally, discuss each statement as a whole class, incorporating the key points below if relevant.

Key points:

- Poverty in the UK is relative (based on comparisons of what would be considered necessary to live a life of the standard that is 'normal' for that particular society). The vast majority of people in the UK do not live in absolute poverty. If they do it may be because of reasons such as poor mental health. People might seem relatively poor if they cannot do what everyone around them can afford to do.
- Someone living in poverty in the UK might still look relatively rich to someone living in one of the poorest countries in the world.
- Many people argue that money alone does not guarantee happiness. They say that if you are unhappy without money, you will still be unhappy with it. Others say it is better to be rich and unhappy than poor and unhappy! Some religions cite that wanting things causes us to suffer and makes us unhappy. They say that if we can learn to be happy without material wealth that is very special and will make a person happy. Happiness can be obtained more meaningfully through achievements, good friendships and having a sense of humour rather than owning lots of possessions.
- The media are always portraying the lives of the rich and famous. This can make people unrealistically aspire to be rich and famous. Very few people achieve fame and extreme wealth – so this means a lot of people are disappointed.
- Many people feel there is a duty to help poor people. Most religions, some charities, some rich people and some celebrities dedicate time and money to relieving poverty.
- If money grew on trees nobody would have the incentive to do anything, things would not be made and jobs would not get done. This highlights the fact that just giving people money is not a long-term solution to tackling poverty.

Support/extension:

- Less able pupils could have the statements read for them and mark a cross on an imaginary spectrum under the statement to indicate how much they agree or disagree with each one.
- Pupils could take these statements home and discuss them with their parent/carer.
- Pupils could explore the idea of what does make people happy.
- Pupils could explore the idea of how long lasting their happiness is when they receive a gift compared with when they achieve something they once found difficult to do.

Type of activity:
Case study and discussion

Learning objective:
to consider what it means to live in relative poverty in the UK (from a child's perspective).

Resources:
'Case study: Chelsea's story' on the CD-ROM and Pupil activity sheet 7 'Chelsea's story. Questions for discussion' (p35); one of each per pair

What does it mean to live in relative poverty in this country? Chelsea's story

What to do:

Please be aware that distancing techniques have been used in this activity and it is important that the activity remains focused on Chelsea and not on individuals in your class. If you have a child named 'Chelsea' in your class, it would be wise to change the name of the child in the story.

1 Remind pupils of the difference between relative and absolute poverty. Explain that in the UK very, very few people live without their basic needs being met (e.g., food, healthcare, somewhere to live, education etc.). Those very few that fail to have these basic needs met usually do so because of reasons that mean they cannot access help and support appropriately (e.g. poor mental health). Explain that poverty in the UK is quite different from absolute poverty in some of the world's countries (where many people do not have clean water, enough food, healthcare etc.). Explain that poverty in the UK is about people not being able to afford things that they see most other people being able to afford.

2 Give pairs of pupils a copy of the sheet 'Case study: Chelsea's story' from the CD-ROM. Read Chelsea's story to the class. Ask pupils if there are any words in the text that they do not understand (e.g. **interest**) and provide a simple explanation for any words they highlight.

3 Explain that many children in this country live in families that do not have a lot of money.

Consolidate the details of the story by asking pupils the following questions:

- How many people are there in Chelsea's family? (4)
- How old is Chelsea? (10)
- What unexpected cost did Chelsea mention? (the washing machine breaking)
- What did Ben do to his trousers? (ripped them)
- Where did they find a new pair? (in a charity shop)
- How does Chelsea's mum pay for birthday presents? (with a **credit card**)
- Who, other than the family, do they have round to help them celebrate birthdays? (neighbours: Jane and her son Oscar)
- Who do they swap houses with when they go on holiday? (Uncle Jason)
- Where does Uncle Jason live? (by the sea)

4 Ask pairs of pupils to answer the questions on the sheet 'Chelsea's story. Questions for discussion' (p35). Discuss their answers as a whole class. Here are some possible answers:

1 Chelsea is the eldest child, so her mum probably talks to her about her money worries a lot. When there is very little money, a person needs to think about how they spend it very carefully and therefore they probably think about it more than people with more money.

2
- She is careful to bring up the topic of school trip money when her mum is in a good mood.
- She looks after her clothes.
- She avoids bringing friends home for tea.
- She tries to tell her mum that she doesn't need lots of presents.

3
- Not doing lots of things at the weekend like her friends
- Having to worry about money for school trips
- Owning only a few clothes
- Not being able to bring friends home for tea
- Not having a birthday party

- Worrying about the cost of presents
- Having a holiday in the same place each year
- Being so aware of money
- Being concerned about her mum's money worries

4 Teasing someone because their family does not have much money is extremely unkind and this needs to be stressed. Comments that might stop the teasing could:

- state clearly how inappropriate and unkind it is to tease someone for any difference (real or perceived), e.g.,

  "It is wrong to tease people."

  "If someone is different from you, you should never pick on that difference – that's prejudice."

- encourage **empathy**, e.g.,

  "Imagine how you would feel if you were Chelsea."

- celebrate the fact that we are not all the same and we have different strengths, e.g.,

  "We all have different things happening in our lives. It's our personalities and achievements that make us who we are."

Dissuade pupils from challenging the teasing with retaliating put downs, making comparisons or comments that refer to or patronise Chelsea's social circumstance.

Key points:

- According to 'Make Child Poverty History', approximately 1 in 3 children in the UK live in relative poverty. In reality this means that children miss out on many activities and possessions that some of their peers take for granted (e.g., birthday celebrations, bicycles).
- Poverty is a somewhat taboo subject. Unless the topic is discussed, **stigma** and prejudice will remain.
- Prejudice itself can contribute to increasing the likelihood of many of the negative outcomes a child living in poverty is susceptible to (e.g., leaving school without qualifications, obtaining a low paid job, poor mental and physical health outcomes).
- Pupils from financially disadvantaged backgrounds can sometimes experience stigmatisation without awareness that it is happening. In ensuring the needs of all vulnerable pupils are addressed, it is important to investigate and combat any kind of stigmatisation.
- Relative poverty is very much about whether or not a person can access those things that most people around them appear to be accessing. If you cannot afford something that everyone else around you can afford, this can make you feel excluded.

Support/extension:

- Less able pupils could draw the things they believe Chelsea would like to be able to do or have (e.g., have a birthday celebration with friends, have friends round after school, own lots of clothes).
- Pupils can investigate further stories of children experiencing relative poverty in the UK at: http://news.bbc.co.uk/cbbcnews/hi/specials/2006/the_wrong_trainers/default.stm
- Ask pupils, 'How could you be a good friend to Chelsea?' In answering this question, encourage pupils to empathise and not patronise. For example: which of the following comments do you think Chelsea would be most happy to hear?

  "I guess being poor and unable to buy what you want must be terrible. I can't imagine it – it must be awful. It must mean you are always missing out – that must make your life really hard." OR

  "I am sorry your mum couldn't afford the new trainers you wanted. Never mind, there's more to you than the shoes you wear."

  Pupils can empathise by imagining both comments being made to them and considering which they would most like to hear.

- You could ask pupils to empathise further with Chelsea by splitting the class into two groups: half being Chelsea and half being someone from a well-off family (Katie). Allocate the roles carefully. Ask the following questions, and if pupils think their answer would be 'yes', ask them to step forward (this highlights the difference between the two children).

1 Do you never really think about how your parents spend your money?

2 Do you have birthday parties?

3 Do you have a lot of outfits to choose from when you go to a party?

4 Do you get what you ask for at Christmas?

5 Is paying for school trips never a problem?

6 Do you get pocket money?

7 Have you joined any clubs, e.g. weekend clubs?

Each time the pupils decide to step forward or not, they are imagining being in the shoes of their character. This method can be used to consider in more depth how Chelsea would feel.

Type of activity
Poster making

Resources:
a selection of pages from fashion magazines

Learning objective
to consider how the media portrays people and the impact this has on our idea of normality and subsequently **success**.

What does a 'normal' person look like?

What to do:

1 Collect a selection of magazine pages with adverts, e.g. adverts from glossy magazines aimed at adult and teenage females and males. Share some of the pages out amongst pairs of pupils.

2 Ask pupils to produce a poster that shows what these magazines would lead us to believe was a 'normal' man and a 'normal' woman – if such a thing did actually exist – which it doesn't! Encourage pupils to collage the pictures from the magazines and to write on their posters any thoughts they have about the 'normal' people and their:

- clothes
- hobbies
- wealth
- holidays
- cars
- relationships
- homes
- happiness
- jobs
- age
- possessions
- lifestyle

If pupils cannot find an image that portrays any of the above exactly, encourage them to make details up (e.g. I think this man would drive a sports car). Recalling TV adverts can help with this.

3 Lead a class discussion about the images pupils have chosen, based on the following questions:
- How often does the media show us this idea of a 'normal' person?
- Do we think of these 'magazine people' as successful?
- Do you think people want to be like the men and women in magazines, pop stars and famous people?
- How might a person feel if they compared themselves and their life to these people?
- Do we think people can be successful if they are nothing like these people? If so, how?

Key points:

- Poverty in the UK is based on relative measures, i.e. someone who is considered to be living in poverty in the UK goes without things that are considered essential to a life that is of an acceptable standard in the UK.
- People are bombarded with this narrow idea of success. Such images can impact on people's self worth if

they have not achieved this particularly prevalent image of success.

- Some people argue that such powerful messages have led some people into **debt**.
- Some examples of how success could be measured, aside from by wealth, are: personal achievements, becoming good at something, getting better at something you find difficult, sticking at something, attaining happiness, feeling positive about your life, things people have complimented you on, having friends you enjoy being with, creating

something, having good ideas, being self-aware, etc.

Support/extension:

- Pupils could make a success advert that 'sells' an idea that is not based on wealth.
- Pupils could add 'graffiti' to a magazine advert that makes the person appear more 'real', e.g. a pile of washing behind them, a thought bubble showing that they are worried about the gas bill, toothpaste on their top, etc.

ACTIVITY 4

Type of activity:
Fact sheet with questions for consideration

Resources:
Pupil activity sheet 8 'Debt – what's it all about?' (p36); one per pair

Learning objective:
to understand borrowing and **debt**, and how it can lead to poverty.

Debt – what's it all about?

What to do:

1 Give pairs of pupils a copy of the sheet 'Debt – what's it all about?' (p36) and read through it.

2 Ask pupils the following questions to check their understanding:

- What does it mean to be 'in debt'?
- If someone buys something with a **credit card**, does the money come out of their bank account? (Explain the difference between credit and debit cards)
- What is the name given to the extra money people have to pay back when they borrow money from a credit card? (**interest**)
- How can a person avoid paying interest even if they have used a credit card? (pay the money back immediately)
- If Mr Pain waited a year to pay back his debt, how much would he have paid for his sofa? (£496)
- What is the average household debt in the UK (not counting mortgages)? (£9633)
- How much interest does the average household pay each year? (£3930)

3 As a whole class, discuss the questions at the bottom of the sheet.

  1 Why do you think some people believe getting in debt is a bad thing to do?

Possible answers include:

- you can end up paying far more than the original cost/amount borrowed because of interest
- paying with a card can seem like you are not spending real money and it's easy to just borrow more and more in the moment without thinking about the difficulties it might create in the future if you are not able to afford to pay it back
- money and debt is one of the main causes of arguments that adult couples have
- being in debt can be very stressful for some people.

  2 Why do you think Mr Pain used his credit card to buy the sofa?

Possible answers include:

- he wanted the sofa now and put off thinking about paying the money back until later
- he had not saved up money for the sofa.

  3 What advice would you give to Mr Pain?

Possible answers include:

- it's more straightforward and cheaper to save up money to buy things as you do not have to pay interest. You also know that you can definitely afford what you are buying.

- It can be very tempting to buy things with credit because you can buy what you want immediately and don't have to wait to save up for something. Some people argue that the banks lend their money far too easily, which encourages people to get into debt and owe money that they cannot really afford to pay back.
- Some people never get into debt and therefore have never paid interest.
- Some households spend a lot of money each month just maintaining a debt and never actually paying it off.
- Interest payments can mean some families do not have the cash to spend on essential items.
- Some people say that saving up to buy something (which requires patience) rather than borrowing money, is preferable because you avoid having to make interest payments and you know that you can afford what you have saved up for.

Support/extension:

- Pupils could use the Internet to investigate companies that lend money, and calculate how much they would owe different companies on a £1000 loan if they did not pay it back for a year. Don't forget to remind pupils that they will pay interest on any interest that builds up.
- Pupils could explore personal stories of debt on the Internet such as those found at http://news.bbc.co.uk/1/hi/programmes/5005374.stm.
- Pupils could write a leaflet to help people understand debt and its potential dangers.
- Pupils could search the Internet for deals where savings actually earn interest and find the best deal. The class could compete to find the greatest amount that could be earnt on £1000 in one year.
- There are several websites that help pupils to develop economic wellbeing and financial capability, for example: http://www.pfeg.org

ACTIVITY 5

What could be done about poverty in the UK?

Type of activity:
Discussing and ordering

Resources:
Pupil activity sheet 9 'What could be done about poverty in the UK?' (p37); one per pair: scissors

Learning objective:
to understand how poverty could be tackled through decisions the government make, but that it cannot be solved overnight.

What to do:

1 Give pairs of pupils a copy of the sheet 'What could be done about poverty in the UK?' (p37). Read it with the whole group and use the Word bank to help ensure pupils understand each of the cards.

2 Ask pupils to discuss in pairs how each of the ideas could help to stop child poverty, and what might prevent each of the ideas from happening.

3 Then ask them to cut out the eight cards and to order them from the idea that could happen most quickly to prevent child poverty to the idea that would require the longest time to put in place.

4 As a class, discuss the order pupils have chosen. The following considerations can be used to guide the discussion.

Idea	Notes
A) Developing better jobs with chances to be promoted	• This is not a simple solution but some places have tackled this by enticing new businesses into the area and training people who are not employed. • Companies and organisations would have to be persuaded to offer promotions.
B) Providing cheaper and better childcare	• This would cost the government money as it would need to contribute to make it cheaper. • In some places childcare is very hard to find – it's possible that not enough people want to be a childminder or nursery worker.
C) Helping children and young people to raise their aspirations.	• This is a long-term solution as it helps people to help themselves. • How can **aspirations** be raised? Sometimes, just being aware of the choices available can develop pupils' aspirations and/or link the work they do at school with the idea that this will give them more career choices when they are older.
D) Making education as good as it can be for everyone	• There are clear links between doing well at school and reducing the chances of living in poverty. • Some people argue that schools only focus on academic subjects and could do more to support less academic pupils find skills they can excel in.
E) Providing better and cheaper homes	• There is a shortage of homes in the UK. More homes would improve the overall standards of living conditions. • This would cost the government a lot of money.
F) Increasing the minimum wage (£5.80 an hour in October 2010)	• This would mean people on low paid jobs would be guaranteed a better wage. • Some people argue that this costs businesses too much money and makes them more likely to fail because they have to spend so much in wages.
G) Improving funding for schools in poor areas	• This would hopefully improve education in these schools and increase their pupils' chances of doing well. • This would cost the government more money than they already allocate to education.

H) Providing more support in schools for children from the poorest backgrounds	• The extra support these children received would have to be well designed to have a positive impact on reducing the chance of the pupils living in poverty. • Some people might argue this was unfair. • This targeted work might cause stigmatisation. • This would cost the government money.

Key points:

• In ordering the suggestions from the quickest to the most long-term solutions pupils will consider each solution. The ultimate order they produce is not significant as no 'correct order' exists. Quicker solutions might include A and G. The rest would be longer-term solutions (i.e. they could not happen overnight).

• This activity highlights that poverty:
  • does not have one single solution
  • cannot be eliminated overnight
  • is about helping people to help themselves so they can contribute to society
  • has solutions, but they usually cost

money and need careful planning if they are to work
  • can only be tackled if the governmen makes it a priority.

Support/extension:

• Less able pupils could be given fewer cards to consider (e.g., A, C, E, F, G).
• Pupils could consider the question:
• Why is solving poverty not just about handing out money to everyone? (it would cost too much, it would only be a short-term solution, the money would run out, a country needs people to contribute to production/society to 'work', handing out money could encourage people to do nothing, etc).

ACTIVITY 6

Child poverty – so how's it going?

Type of activity:

Newspaper report; true/false quiz and discussion

Resources:

'Child poverty – so how's it going?' article on the CD-ROM and Pupil activity sheet 10 'Child poverty: Quiz' p38); one of each per pair
A copy of the definitions below – one per pair.

Learning objective:

to consider the government's target of getting rid of child poverty by 2020, the progress it has made and opinions on how the target could be met.

What to do:

1 Give pairs of pupils a copy of the sheet 'Child poverty – so how's it going?' from the CD-ROM. Read through the article 'Number of children living in poverty rises'. Ask pairs of pupils to underline six words or phrases that they do not understand. To dissuade pupils from only underlining words/phrases in the first paragraph, allocate different paragraphs to different pairs of pupils. When pupils have finished underlining ask them to make a guess at the meaning of their six words/phrases. Hand out the following definitions and ask pupils to check whether their guesses were correct.

Some definitions

• Target: the point that you are trying to get to
• Progress – achieving what you are trying to do
• Uprate – increase
• Benefit system – the system that pays money to support people in times of difficulty (e.g. when they are out of work)

• moral leadership – the people in charge making decisions that are considered to be 'good' and 'proper'.
• Tight budget – when there is not much money around
• National wealth – how much money a country has overall
• Interim target – a target on the way to the final one

You could also aid understanding by asking pupils to give a summary of each paragraph or matching each of the following summaries to the correct paragraph.

1 The number of children living in poverty has increased in the last couple of years.

2 Anti-poverty campaigners say £3 billion is needed for the Prime Minister's anti-poverty target to be met.

3 The Work and Pensions Secretary said there had been progress and many more children would be living in poverty if the government had done nothing.

4 The Child Poverty Action Group said the government leaders have let us down and it is time for the government to pay more money if we are to stop children living in poverty.

5 Barnardo's said that it is ridiculous that there are children living in poverty despite being the world's fifth richest country.

6 One Labour MP said it is great that the government is trying to do something about poverty but unless they change what they are doing, they will not reach their targets.

7 Numbers of children living in poverty are rising but the number of adults living in poverty has remained the same.

2 Give pairs of pupils the sheet 'Child poverty: Quiz?' (p38) and ask them to complete the true and false quiz based on the article. Go through the answers as a class:

1 True

2 False: In 2008, the number of children living in poverty had gone *up* since 2005/6.

3 False: The government had set itself a target of getting rid of child poverty by *2020.*

4 False: Anti-poverty campaigners say **£3** billion needs to be spent to get rid of child poverty in the UK.

5 False: In 1999, **3.4** million children were living in poverty.

6 True

7 True

8 False: Barnados said it is shameful that so many children live in poverty in the **fifth** richest country in the world.

9 True

10 False: It looks like the government will *not* reach its target of getting rid of child poverty by 2020 if it carries on doing the same as it has done.

3 If time allows, ask pupils why they believe the government has not given enough money to combat child poverty. Use some of the key points below to guide the discussion.

Key points:

- Getting rid of child poverty is a complex issue and will not be solved by just throwing money at the problem.
- The work the government did first to get rid of poverty will have helped the 'easy to reach' families (e.g. some working parents/carers will have increased their household income). Families still living in poverty will be harder to reach. They will take longer to lift out of poverty and more consideration is needed to work out how best to do this.
- Some people would argue that the government is not bothered enough about child poverty because if it was, more effort, time and money would have been spent on tackling the problem and much more progress would have been made.
- If more people showed they supported the need to combat child poverty, the government might 'sit up and listen', as they rely on people's votes to remain in power.

Support/extension:

- You could support less able pupils by underlining the details that need to be changed in the quiz.
- Pupils could write a letter to their local MP or local council explaining their concern that not enough is being done about child poverty.
- More able pupils could discuss what they would actually do if they were Prime Minister.

Type of activity:
Case study: from poverty to wealth
Resources:
'A genuine rags to riches tale' article on the CD-ROM; one per pair
Learning objective:
to consider **aspirations**.

From rags to riches – let's look at aspirations

What to do:

1 Give pairs of pupils a copy of the sheet 'A genuine rags to riches tale' (on the CD-ROM) and read through the article. Ask pupils the following questions:

- What did Raj's father say was important if you were to do well in business? (education)
- What did Raj's two sisters do that was unusual for girls in India? (go to university in the 1950s)
- What was Raj's first job? (a basic factory job)
- What was the first thing Raj sold? (ice cream)
- Was Raj a hard worker? (yes)
- After running the market stall, what was Raj able to open? (a high-street shop)
- Name a shop that his successful business now supplies. (BHS, House of Fraser)

2 Explain that there are many very wealthy people who started out in poverty and/or did not do particularly well at school (e.g. Alan Sugar, Richard Branson, Tom Cruise, Steven Spielberg). Ask pupils to imagine such a person and discuss in pairs the qualities they think that person would have, e,g. determined, hardworking, have aspirations. If they are willing to share their experiences, you could include examples of teachers or members of the local community that did not do well at school or lived in childhood poverty and are now more successful than their early years might have suggested. They do not necessarily have to be very wealthy.

3 Ask pupils to consider how they would hope to answer the following questions in the future:

- Have you been to university or college? If so, what did you study?
- Do you have children and if so, how old are they?
- Do you have a job and if so, what is it?
- Do you enjoy your job?
- Do you work hard?
- Are you sensible with money?
- Where do you live?
- Are you fit and healthy? If so, what do you do to keep fit and healthy?
- Do you still have ambitions and if so, what are they?

4 Ask pupils to write about and draw their aspirations on a piece of paper.

Key points:

- People who succeed financially tend to be driven, determined, have clear visions about what they want to do, work hard, are not set back too much by disappointment, see opportunities, are ambitious, use their imagination and take risks.
- The government has cited raising aspirations as a means of impacting upon poverty prevention. Ambitions need not be about making a lot of money but they can help people to aspire to reach their potential.

Support/extension:

- Pupils could consider future jobs that they would like to do and the skills, qualities and qualifications that would be needed to do those jobs successfully.
- A school could hold an aspirations day by inviting parents/carers, local business people and/or public sector workers to come to school and talk about their careers.

What do people say about poverty?

Type of activity:
Discussion and agreement spectrum

Resources:
Pupil activity sheet 11 'What do people say about poverty?' (p39); one per pair

Learning objective:
to consider conflicting viewpoints about poverty in the UK.

What to do:

1 Give pairs of pupils a copy of the sheet 'What do people say about poverty?' (p39). Read the different views and ask pupils to underline any of the statements they agree with.

2 Open up a discussion using an agreement spectrum. Firstly, make the following statements:
- If people don't have money, it is their own fault.
- The government needs to do more to try and stop poverty in this country.
- Preventing poverty is not straightforward.
- It is wrong that some people earn lots of money while others live in poverty.
- If you make people pay high taxes, they will go and live in another country.

Now ask pupils to stand on an imaginary line from 'strongly agree' to strongly disagree' depending on how they feel about what has been said. NB: if space is tight, ask pupils to raise their arms to demonstrate how they feel about each statement, e.g. raising your arm fully means you strongly agree with the statement, not raising it at all means you strongly disagree and raising it halfway means you neither agree or disagree. Once pupils have decided where to stand (or how much to raise their arm), invite discussion by asking, 'Would anyone like to say something about where they have stood (or where they have positioned their arm)?' Allow pupils to move if their opinion changes as the discussion progresses.

Hopefully pupils will explore views and learn from each other. As a facilitator of the discussion, try to remain impartial if there is a spread of views or play devil's advocate and challenge pupils' views if they are all in agreement or if pupils are not really challenging each other.

Key points:

- Homelessness is briefly touched upon in this activity. Homelessness can happen for a variety of reasons and does not just refer to people who 'sleep rough'. Mental health issues, being evicted or running away from the parental home, failing to access the welfare system, leaving care, arriving in the UK or a new place looking for work are just some reasons why people can be vulnerable to homelessness.
- People do show different levels of concern about the issue of poverty. Apathy about the issue might be one of the reasons why it has never been fully addressed.
- Many people would argue that being able to earn a lot of money is a right and people should not be criticised for financial **success**. The drive to make money provides a reason why lots of things get done, invented and produced!
- Poverty is a complex issue and no single solution will prevent it.

Support/extension:

- Pupils could write down their own views about poverty.
- Pupils could discuss how they feel and what they think when they see a homeless person.
- Pupils could discuss whether or not they believe relative poverty could be eliminated.
- Teachers could add their own personal viewpoint for pupils to discuss.

 **SHEET** **6** # What do you think about poverty and wealth in the UK?

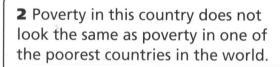

How much do you agree or disagree with each of these statements? Write your ideas down in note form.

1 Most people in this country have enough to eat, have a home, have an education and can see a doctor if they need to.

2 Poverty in this country does not look the same as poverty in one of the poorest countries in the world.

3 You might feel poor if you do not have enough money to pay for things that you see everyone else in the country doing.

4 Adverts on the television can make people want things they do not have enough money to buy.

5 All rich people are really happy.

6 Everyone wants to be rich and famous.

8 Most people in this country think having lots of money is really important.

7 People who have very little money should be helped by people who have lots of money.

10 If money grew on trees, we would all be OK.

9 If I was given lots of money, I know exactly what I would do with it.

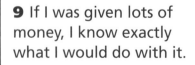

Chelsea's story: Questions for discussion

1 Do you think Chelsea thinks a lot about money for a ten-year-old child? If so, why do you think this is?

_____

_____

_____

_____

_____

_____

2 Chelsea is very careful about a lot of things because her family does not have a lot of money. List three things she is careful about.

1 _____

_____

2 _____

_____

3 _____

_____

3 What things might make Chelsea feel 'different and left out'? Find three things.

1 _____

_____

2 _____

_____

3 _____

_____

4 Some people are teased because they do not have a lot of money. If someone teased Chelsea, what would you say to them?

_____

_____

_____

_____

_____

_____

Debt – what's it all about?

People are said to be in debt when they borrow money – usually to buy something. When someone borrows money, they have to pay it back. If they borrow money from a bank or use a credit card, they can end up paying back much more than they actually spent or borrowed in the first place.

One of the easiest ways for people to borrow money is to use a credit card when they pay for something. Here is an example to show how a credit card works:

Mr Pain used his Starshop credit card to buy a new sofa for £400. This means that the company Starshop (that gave Mr Pain his credit card) have paid for the sofa, so Mr Pain now owes Starshop £400. If Mr Pain pays £400 to Starshop in the next few days he will only have to pay the £400.

However, if Mr Pain takes longer to pay the money, Starshop will make Mr Pain not only pay back the £400 he owes them, they will also ask for interest. Interest is the money they will charge Mr Pain for borrowing the £400, which could be about £8 for every month he does not pay. If Mr Pain chose not to pay for a year, he would have to pay back the £400 plus £96.

So, if he took a year to pay back Starshop, Mr Pain would have paid £496 for his sofa instead of £400.

According to Credit Action in 2008:

The average household debt in the UK is £9633 (not including mortgages – the money borrowed to buy houses).

The average interest paid by each household on their total debt is approximately £3930 each year.

The average household debt will increase by more than £7.20 each day.

The Citizen Advice Bureau (an organisation that gives people advice about all kinds of issues) dealt with 4760 debt problems every day during the last 12 months.

The number of people in debt by over £100,000 has doubled in recent years.

Now think about these questions:

1 Why do you think some people believe getting in debt is a bad thing to do?

2 Why do you think Mr Pain used his credit card to buy the sofa?

3 What advice would you give to Mr Pain?

What could be done about poverty in the UK?

In 1999 the prime minister at the time, Tony Blair, made a promise to end child poverty by 2020.

Here is how the government is already trying to do this and some other ideas that have been suggested:

A Developing better jobs with chances to be promoted	**B** Providing cheaper and better childcare
C Helping children and young people to raise their aspirations	**D** Making education as good as it can be for everyone
E Providing better and cheaper homes	**F** Increasing the minimum wage (£5.80 an hour in October 2010)
G Improving funding for schools in poor areas	**H** Providing more support in schools for children from the poorest backgrounds

A) Take each idea one at a time and answer the following questions.

1) How might this idea help to stop poverty?
2) What might stop this idea from happening?

B) Sort the cards in order from the idea you think could happen most quickly to prevent poverty, to the one you think would take the longest.

Word bank

government – the people making decisions about how the country is run. Tax (money) is paid to the government and they decide how the tax is spent

promoted – to be given a job with more responsibility that is usually paid better than the job you left behind

funding – money a place or organisation (e.g., a school) receives

aspirations – a person's hopes and expectations for their future

minimum – the lowest amount

wage – the money a person is paid for working

childcare – children being looked after by a nursery or childminder, usually so the parent/carer can go to work

Child poverty: Quiz

> Put a circle around T or F to show whether each statement is true or false. If the answer is false, change the statement to make it true.

1) In 2008, 2.9 million children in the UK were living in poverty.

T / F _____

_____

2) In 2008, the number of children living in poverty was lower than in 2005/2006.

T / F _____

_____

3) The government had set itself a target of getting rid of child poverty by 2010.

T / F _____

_____

4) Anti-poverty campaigners say £50 billion needs to be spent to get rid of child poverty in the UK.

T / F _____

_____

5) In 1999, 35 million children were living in poverty.

T / F _____

_____

6) The government says that if it had done nothing to try and improve the situation, there would be 1.7 million more children living in poverty.

T / F _____

_____

7) The Child Poverty Action Group says that government leaders are to blame for the increase in numbers of children living in poverty because they have not done enough.

T / F _____

_____

8) Barnados said it is shameful that so many children live in poverty in the tenth richest country in the world.

T / F _____

_____

9) Labour MP Frank Field, says that it is great that the government is trying to get rid of child poverty but what they have done so far has not worked, so they need to change what they are doing if they are going to succeed.

T / F _____

_____

10) It looks like the government will reach its target of getting rid of child poverty by 2020 if it carries on doing the same as it has done.

T / F _____

_____

What do people say about poverty?

There are many different views about poverty, its causes and what might prevent it.

Underline any of the things the people below have said that you agree with.

I think that wherever you go there will be people who are well off and people who are not – it's just how it has always been. You just need to look after yourself and make sure you are OK.

I think poverty itself can make it hard for people to get a job because their confidence gets knocked and they end up feeling like no one would give them a job.

I think poverty could be ended for once and for all if the government made it a priority. There is more than enough to go round but some people get much more than their fair share.

I think poor people are just lazy. There's work if they want it. I think the benefit system stops people bothering to look for work – because they just get given money for doing nothing.

I think people become homeless mostly because they are mentally ill. Surely no one would choose to be homeless. These people should be helped.

I think people end up living in poverty for a number of reasons. Getting away from poverty is not as straightforward as just going out and finding a well-paid job. Single parents can struggle to have a job and look after their children, for example, or some people who messed up at school find it hard to get a good job. Some people are quick to judge but judgement never helps anyone.

Many children live in poverty. You cannot say to them that it's their fault – even if you are someone who goes around blaming people.

I don't care about people I can't see.

Poverty can cause crime and poor health so surely everyone should be concerned about getting rid of it.

SECTION 3

Global poverty

This section aims to help pupils understand poverty and inequality issues around the world.

Key questions

- What is global inequality?
- How does global poverty impact on people?
- Are all less materialistic lifestyles considered to be a life of poverty?
- What is life as a street child in India like?
- What are the key issues of living in poverty in Africa?
- How can people living in poverty be helped?
- What is Fairtrade and what does it do?
- What happens or could happen if a government was committed to combating poverty?

Learning objectives of the activities

- to consider global inequality.
- to explore the different causes of global poverty and their effects, and to realise how complex this issue is, with no simple solution.
- to consider how lifestyles that might seem quite different from our own are not necessarily considered to be a life of poverty.
- to consider the impact of extreme poverty for some children in India, and to empathise with a street child.
- to consider what living in poverty on the African continent is like and how it compares to life in the UK.
- to consider how people living in poverty worldwide can be helped
- to consider how political will is needed to effectively address the issues of poverty.
- to consider Fairtrade, its impact and its relationship to the consumer.
- to consider what would need to happen to combat poverty.

Learning objectives from the non-statutory guidance for PSHE and Citizenship:

Pupils should be taught:
1 a) to talk and write about their opinions, and explain their views, on issues that affect themselves and society
2 a) to research, discuss and debate topical issues, problems and events
2 e) to reflect on spiritual, moral, social, and cultural issues, using imagination to understand other people's experiences
2 h) to recognise the role of voluntary, community and pressure groups
2 j) that resources can be allocated in different ways and that these economic choices affect individuals, communities and the sustainability of the environment
4 a) that their actions affect themselves and others, to care about other people's feelings and to try to see things from their points of view
4 b) to think about the lives of people living in other places and times, and people with different values and customs
4 e) to recognise and challenge stereotypes

SPEAKING AND LISTENING

Listening

Pupils should be taught to:

2a. identify the gist of an account or key points in a discussion and evaluate

2b. ask relevant questions to clarify, extend and follow up ideas

2e. respond to others appropriately, taking into account what they say

Group discussion and interaction

Pupils should be taught to:

3a. make contributions relevant to the topic and take turns in discussion

3c. qualify or justify what they think after listening to others' accounts

Drama

4a. create, adapt and sustain different roles, individually and in groups

4c. use dramatic techniques to explore characters and issues [for example, hot seating, flashback]

READING

Understanding texts

Pupils should be taught to:

2a. use inference and deduction

2b. look for meaning beyond the literal

Reading for information

Pupils should be taught to:

3a. scan texts to find information

3b. skim for gist and overall impression

3c. obtain specific information through detailed reading

3g. consider an argument critically

Non-fiction and non-literary texts

Pupils should be taught to:

5g. engage with challenging and demanding subject matter.

WRITING

Composition

Pupils should be taught to:

1a. choose form and content to suit a particular purpose [for example, notes to read or organise thinking, plans for action, poetry for pleasure]

1c. use language and style that are appropriate to the reader

1d. use and adapt the features of a form of writing, drawing on their reading

1e. use features of layout, presentation and organisation effectively

Planning and drafting

Pupils should be taught to:

2a. plan – note and develop initial ideas

2b. draft – develop ideas from the plan into structured written text

2c. revise – change and improve the draft

2d. proofread – check the draft for errors, omissions and repetitions

2e. present – prepare a neat, correct and clear final copy

Key Vocabulary

- global poverty
- inequality
- governments
- Fairtrade
- exploitation
- subsidised
- shanty town

Imagine this...

Type of activity:
Exploring a metaphor –
a room
Resources:
Pupil activity sheet 12
'Imagine this...' (p54);
one per pair
Learning objective:
to consider global
inequality.

What to do:

1 Give pairs of pupils a copy of the sheet 'Imagine this...' (p54). Read the description to the class.

2 Ask groups of pupils to discuss the four questions on the sheet, making brief notes of their agreed answers on a sheet of paper. Some example answers might be:

1 You would be very unlikely to find such a contrast co-existing in the same room.

2 Guilty, perhaps protective of their things, sad, want to do something to help..

3 They probably feel it is unjust, they would suffer more for seeing so much food – especially food being thrown away.

4 If these people were really in the same room, what happened would probably depend on how they all felt about each other. It might be that:

• water from the tap is shared with everyone

• everyone shares the food

• all the luxury in the corner of the room is spread out so everyone can share

• the food is shared, but not with everyone because they are scared it won't go far when it is shared; the people living in luxury might choose to only help the children for example.

• the four people might guard their luxury and refuse to share

• the people living in the shabby section of the room might try to steal things from the luxury section of the room.

3 Explain that this room could be a metaphor for what is happening in the world. The developed world is living in relative luxury, consuming vast quantities of (and actually wasting) food and materials while people in the developing world often fail to get enough to eat. However, unlike in this room, we are not always aware of this starvation. Ask the pupils if seeing the starving people would make us more likely to do something to help them.

4 Explore the metaphor further using the key points below.

5 Finish by asking the same groups of pupils to discuss the following question:

What do you think would need to happen to ensure everyone in the room helped each other out? For example:

• they would need to feel they had enough to share and their lifestyle would not be hugely changed,

• they would need to feel connected with and responsible for the people not eating

• there would need to be a strong sense that things should be fair

• there would need to be an understanding that hunger can impact on people's behaviour and 'scruples' (see Maslow's hierarchy of needs page 12)

6 Ask pupils if their answers could be applied to the worldwide situation of inequality.

Key points:

• As this metaphor highlights, even if people in the room could just hand over food to those without any, it still might not happen because people might be reluctant to share. This could be said of the developed world showing reluctance to share enough with the developing world to prevent starvation.

• Sorting out food shortages cannot be as simple as handing it over to those people in the world without it – although this does provide short-term relief from starvation and is often necessary.

• Plans and financial aid that help to develop agriculture in developing countries will have a long-term impact on relieving starvation. This metaphor can be extended by asking pupils if they think it would be better if the four living in luxury just kept handing their food over to those without food or if the larger group were supported to grow their own food.

- Pupils could draw a picture of the room on a poster to raise people's awareness of world inequality. They could include thought bubbles to show what people might be thinking.
- If the teacher feels comfortable facilitating a roleplay, it could be used to explore this situation further and to encourage empathy. The class could be split into two groups – one quarter

living in luxury and the rest in poverty – existing in this room together. You could ask those living in luxury to go about preparing a meal, while the rest watch. You could then go into role as a reporter investigating this metaphor and ask the pupils living in poverty what they would like to say to those preparing a meal (you might like to take one comment at a time). You could then ask those living in luxury how each comment would make them respond. NB: It is crucial to de-role pupils after such an activity, e.g. explain clearly that the roleplay has finished and ask everyone what they had for tea last night to bring them back into the room!

ACTIVITY 2

Causes and effects of poverty

Type of activity:
Table prompting discussion

Resources:
Pupil activity sheet 13 'What causes global poverty?' (p55); one per pair

Learning objective:
to explore the different causes of global poverty and their effects, and to realise how complex this issue is, with no simple solution.

What to do:

This activity encourages pupils to consider some causes of global poverty and also gives an overview of how complex and interconnected the causes of poverty are.

1 Explain to pupils that there is rarely one single cause of poverty. The causes can be complicated and interconnected. For example: a country failing to provide education for its citizens can make individuals less likely to be employed (or use 'educated' methods of industry or farming), which can mean the country has less money (as not much tax is paid) which means it is less likely to have the necessary resources to provide education. So causes and effects of poverty are entwined.

2 Give pairs of pupils a copy of the sheet 'What causes global poverty?' (p55). Ask them to look at the table, and check pupils' understanding of all the causes and effects.

3 Next discuss whether each cause is likely to have more impact on people who are already living in poverty or on wealthy people. Another way to explore this would be to ask: What could/can wealthy people do about each cause of poverty so that it does not really affect them?

4 Ask pairs of pupils to complete the sheet. Some cause–effects links are more obvious than others, but encourage speculation.

5 Once pupils have completed the sheet, take feedback and explore each cause and its related effects using the notes on the next page to help you.

Cause of poverty	Notes
Fuel and food prices going up	This hits the most poor the hardest. Obviously it can mean families do not get enough food. Health can be affected when people choose to feed their children and go without themselves, or because they spend all their money on food and cannot then afford to pay for health treatment if they become sick (healthcare costs money in most other countries). Fuel price rises also mean fertilisers (made from oil products) cost more, thus impacting on the ability to grow more food. Along with transport costs this pushes food prices up further. Food prices can also impact on education because children in some families will be pulled from education to work to earn money for the family and/or school fees can no longer be afforded.
Soil being overused and no longer good for growing crops	This impacts on food provision and has left whole countries short of food and people no longer earning money from farm work. If this happens in a country that exports its food, it can leave the country even poorer.
Wealthy **governments** encouraging farmers to grow cash crops such as biofuels and food for exportation rather than food that would benefit the local people	The pressure to grow cash crops such as biofuels or food that can be exported and sold comes from wealthy countries that pay well. However, not everyone in that country will benefit from the wealth this can create and it also leaves the poorest short of food. Malnutrition affects millions of children around the world.
Diseases like AIDS and malaria that can kill	Diseases like AIDS and malaria can kill. Children are left as orphans. This makes children vulnerable to lack of food, shelter and healthcare. Diseases can also disable people making them unable to earn money. Without money, children are unlikely to be able to prioritise school fees.
Natural disasters – floods, hurricanes	Natural disasters can leave thousands of people with poor food provision, no shelter, lack of healthcare and no ability to earn money. Education is not a priority in times of extreme crisis.
Conflict and war	War can strip people of their homes, their jobs and their education. Many wars cause people to migrate away from their homes which can make them vulnerable to extreme poverty. During wars, governments spend money on weapons rather than things like education, healthcare, etc.
Lack of education	Lack of education can make a person less likely to get a well-paid job, which can make them vulnerable to poverty. Girls in particular are less likely to access education in some parts of the world.
No clean water supply	This can affect health, which in turn can affect the ability to earn money. Everyday thousands of people die because they are drinking water contaminated by dangerous chemicals or sewage.
Corrupt governments that do not care about the people in their country	In some countries there are governments that are too busy dealing with fighting and power struggles to pay attention to supporting a population in need. This can leave people in extreme poverty and starving because it is hard to maintain food supply without stability – growing and transporting food needs time, dedication (a workforce that is not transient) and an effective infrastructure.

Children unable to attend school because they need to work to provide much needed money for their family	This can affect children's health and education. Worldwide, tens of millions of 5 to 14 year olds work. Children tend to be poorly paid, work the longest hours, are treated badly and some jobs lead to stunted growth or have a high risk of harm from accidents.
Climate change	Unpredictable weather is causing an increased number of natural disasters (flooding, droughts, plagues of locusts, hurricanes) which hit the world's poor the hardest as their ability to survive on natural resources is reduced. The World Health Organisation estimates that 150,000 people die each year as a result of climate change.
A country being in debt and having to pay interest	Many countries owe money to the World Bank or to other governments. Paying interest on these debts can prevent countries from being able to spend money on things that can prevent poverty such as education, healthcare, farming developments.

6 Ask pupils to consider each cause of poverty and discuss possible solutions. Explain that this is not easy as the world has not worked it out yet! Possible solutions might include: prioritising clean water supplies, simple, cheap medical treatments that could prevent many illnesses and deaths, education about farming methods that do not leave the soil damaged, world leaders having the political will to consistently take responsibility for poorer countries' wellbeing, fair trade, reducing carbon emissions, etc.

Key points:

- The causes of poverty are complex and vary from region to region, country to country and continent to continent.
- Poverty can make people more vulnerable to further poverty.
- It is nearly always the poorest that suffer most as a result of the causes of poverty.
- Some poverty is a result of irresponsible government policy – within countries and worldwide.
- Poverty can also be caused by **exploitation**. The following description may help pupils understand the term 'exploitation'. Exploitation is where land and/or people are used to make money(usually a lot) for an individual or business. In these cases, there is little consideration for the wellbeing of those people and the land they live on. For example, if people in a factory were paid very little money (not enough to provide for their basic needs) while what they were making in the factory was being sold at very high prices and making the factory owner lots of money – the factory workers would be described as being exploited by the factory owner.
- There are resources enough in the world to prevent extreme poverty. For this to happen, however, requires governments to want to tackle it and to tackle it appropriately. And for governments to want to do anything about it, they need to know that it is a priority for the electorate.

Support/extension:

- For younger or less able pupils, you could reduce the number of causes that you ask them to look at or give them a list of the causes alone and ask pupils to volunteer information about how they think each cause affects poverty.
- Pupils could choose some of the following issues and investigate the work that charities like Oxfam, Plan UK and Save the Children are doing to address them: clean water supplies, food shortages, health provision, education.

It's all relative

Type of activity

Case study: a nomadic lifestyle

Resources:

'Case study: a nomadic lifestyle' on the CD-ROM; one per pair

Learning objective:

to consider how lifestyles that might seem quite different from our own are not necessarily considered to be a life of poverty.

What to do:

1 Give pairs of pupils a copy of the sheet 'Case study: a nomadic lifestyle' from the CD-ROM. Read the sheet and ask small groups of pupils to discuss the questions.

2 Ask each group for feedback from their discussions.

3 Develop the discussion further by asking pupils the following questions:
  • Do you think everyone in the world should have exactly the same lifestyle?
  • Do you think Amineh is proud of the life she leads? Do you think she should be
  • Do you think Amineh longs to own many more possessions and live in a big house?

4 Close the discussion by highlighting some of the key points below.

Key points:

• Amineh has plenty of food, access to clean water, a home, family and friends around her, time to play, education and things to do. She appears to enjoy her life just as it is.

• Amineh lives a lifestyle that in comparison with many people in the developed world would seem basic in terms of material wealth. Amineh's family are unlikely to consider themselves as living in poverty, are likely to feel a strong sense of belonging to their group and feel proud of their way of life. It is only comparisons with other lifestyles that might draw a conclusion that Amineh is living in poverty.

• There is always a danger of patronising people living in poverty or living different lifestyles to our own and of making assumptions about their happiness, their capabilities and their desires.

• Some people might consider the developed world's reliance upon material goods and consumption to be 'missing the point' about what is truly important. Material wealth does not always automatically result in happiness.

Support/extension:

• Pupils could investigate the lives of nomadic people of Africa using the Internet to see if they can find out any more information about their lifestyles.

Street children

What to do:

1 Explain that in India some children end up living on the streets for a variety of reasons. Give pairs of pupils a copy of the sheet 'Case study: Street children in India' from the CD-ROM. Read through it and explain any vocabulary or concepts that pupils do not understand.

2 Then give pairs of pupils a copy of the sheet 'Consider the life of a street child in India' (p56). Ask pairs of pupils to work through questions 1-3. and discuss the pupils' answers as a whole class.

3 Look together at the freeze-frame section of the sheet. If pupils are not used to using freeze-frames, explain what they are to the class:

Freeze-frames are where people show a moment in time as if it were a photograph. Ask pairs of pupils to make up a freeze-frame as outlined on the sheet. Stress that pupils need to try and imagine they really are in the moment of time that their freeze-frame shows, with the thoughts and expressions they think each person would have.

4 When pupils have completed their freeze-frames, ask pairs of pupils to show the class. Ask pupils questions that encourage empathy, such as:

- What are you thinking?
- How are you feeling?
- What are you hoping will happen?
- Is anything bothering you?
- Are you scared of anything?

5 Close the discussion by asking pupils what they think must be the worst thing about being a street child in India. Ask willing pupils to share their views.

Type of activity

Case study, questions and freeze-frame

Resources:

'Case study: Street children in India' on the CD-ROM and Pupil activity sheet 14 'Consider the life of a street child in India' (p56); one of each per pair

Learning objective:

to consider the impact of extreme poverty for some children in India, and to empathise with a street child.

Key points:

- Many countries (e.g. Russia, Romania, Brazil) have street children, mostly in urban areas.
- Children end up living on the streets for many different reasons. These include: poverty, famine, natural disaster, overcrowding in urban areas, war, families breaking down, etc.
- Street children are at risk from many hazards. One extreme example is danger of death from the systematic extermination of street children by 'clean up squads' in Brazil. This concept might be very difficult for pupils in the UK to comprehend so sensitivity needs to be applied if this is described to pupils.
- Solving the problem of children living on the street would require political will and substantial amounts of money. Many countries are unlikely to prioritise this issue in the near future.
- There are many charitable organisations that work to improve the lives of street children.

- This activity highlights how poverty in different countries can be quite different. In some countries, many children live on the street whereas the UK has a welfare system that should mean children in this country never end up living on the streets. NB: some pupils might be aware that some young people do end up on the streets. This is usually because of very complex reasons and/or because those children have somehow been overlooked by the welfare system.

Support/extension:

- Pupils could research information about street children in different countries and the charities that work with them.
- Pupils could fundraise for a charity that supports street children.
- Pupils could draw a storyboard showing an average day in the life of a street child in India. A useful website is http://www.indiastreetchildren.org/

What does poverty look like on the African continent?

Type of activity
Writing a description

Resources:
Pupil activity sheet 15 'What does poverty look like on the African continent?' (p57); one per pair: a map of Africa

Learning objective:
to consider what living in poverty on the African continent is like by exploring one person's direct experience of it and how it compares to life in the UK.

What to do:

1 Show pupils a map of Africa and ask pupils what they know about Africa. Challenge any views that describe Africa just in terms of poverty. Africa has areas of comparative wealth and poverty like all countries worldwide. Show pupils where Liberia, Malawi (and Zimbabwe if Activity 6 is also intended) are on the map.

2 Give pairs of pupils a copy of the sheet 'What does poverty look like on the African continent?' (p57). Read through the sheet and ask pupils to write down three things they learnt or that surprised them from this text. Ask pairs of pupils to share what they wrote.

3 Under the headings of:
- Water
- Food
- Education
- Healthcare
- Daily Lives

ask pupils to write a short piece similar to that on the sheet, describing children in the UK's typical experience of each of these things. Encourage pupils to describe each thing as if they were explaining it to someone who had no knowledge of what happens in the UK. This will highlight how many things we take for granted in this country that are not true for everyone in the world.

4 As a class, discuss the differences between the experiences of people in Africa and in the UK.

Key points:

- African countries do not have a national welfare system to look after people living in poverty, so they are not automatically given relief for their poverty. Therefore the key features of poverty in Africa can seem quite removed from life in the UK.
- Key features of poverty vary from place to place and in extremity on the African continent – as in most places worldwide. For example, in some places poverty might mean little or no food; in other places it could mean no education.
- There is a tendency to patronise those living in poverty and make assumptions about their lives and their aspirations. It is important that pupils do not make assumptions about lifestyles they have not experienced and that they show sensitivity to those experiencing them. For example, Everjoice once overheard reporters describing the daily meal some children in Liberia were

about to eat using very unfavourable terms. Those eating the meal did not appreciate this description of the food they were about to eat and the food that was crucial to their survival.
- Pupils need to realise that this is one person's first-hand experience of poverty on the African continent and that there will be people better and worse off than those Everjoice has described.

Support/extension:

- Pupils should be encouraged to research further to gain a more extensive and representative view of poverty throughout the African continent. They can research poverty in Africa from Internet sources such as http://cozay.com/
- Less able pupils could represent UK life in cartoon form – using stick people and speech bubbles – under the same headings.
- Pupils could illustrate the three points they listed during step 2 of the activity.

Helping people to help themselves

Type of activity
Discussion

Learning objective:
to consider how people living in poverty worldwide can be helped.

What to do:

Ideally, pupils will have completed Activity 5: What does poverty look like on the African continent? before starting this activity.

1 Remind pupils of the issues explored in the activity, 'What does poverty look like on the African continent?' Make sure everyone understands the last paragraph on Pupil activity sheet 15 (p57), 'Helping people to help themselves'.

2 Explain to pupils that Widows and Orphans Relief and Development Trust International (WORD) does not have huge amounts of money. It works by helping people to work together to solve problems. The organisation works directly with people living in poverty, not with **governments**. Share the following examples of how WORD helped people to help themselves:

- In Liberia a group of over 200 widows were asked to bring $5 to a revolving fund (an amount of money that people take take turns to borrow from) that could be borrowed from to solve problems or provide the means to make more money.
- When people in Liberia looked to WORD to provide spoons and bowls to deliver a feeding programme, WORD directed them to each bring a utensil and they soon realised they did not need help.
- In Zimbabwe, a system was set up where widows house stranded widowed women and orphans so that they have somewhere to live.

3 Ask pairs of pupils to discuss the following two questions:

- For each of the examples above, why was it important that people were prepared to work together?
- Why do you think it is better to help people living in poverty by teaching them ways they can help themselves than just handing over money?

4 Take feedback from pairs and expand the discussion using the key points below.

Key points:

- Some people argue that when money is given to some countries' governments to help people living in poverty, much is wasted and does not actually benefit those living in poverty directly.
- Helping people to help themselves makes them independent and able to sustain their own lifestyle and remain out of poverty. If people just relied on money being given to them, they would continually rely on this and this source might not continue indefinitely.

- Emergency relief is still relevant as short-term relief for people not getting enough to eat because of a natural disaster, for example.

Support/extension:

- Pupils can explore anti-poverty websites to find examples of other projects that help people to help themselves so that they do not require continuous support.

Political will – Chavez

What to do:

1 Give pairs of pupils a copy of the sheet 'Case study: Political will – Chavez' from the CD-ROM. Read through the sheet as a class and check pupils' understanding.

2 Ask pupils what they think of recent events in Venezuela.

3 Discuss the following questions as a whole class:

- Chavez decided to spend Venezuela's money on helping those people living in poverty. Did he have to do this? (no)
- When someone is in charge of a country, do you think they will always see that helping poor people is really important? (frequently, not enough, or there would be fewer people worldwide living in poverty)
- Do you think Chavez's actions were unusual? If so why?
- What might have stopped Chavez doing what he did? (he could have been influenced by the country's wealthy not to bother helping the poor; once he was wealthy, he might have developed less concern about other people's poverty; the media (which is often anti-Chavez) might have made him lose confidence in what he was doing)

4 The changes listed on the sheet 'Case Study: Political Will: Chavez' had a huge impact on the lives of those living in the **shanty towns** of Venezuela. Ask small groups of pupils to list what they believe living in a shanty town was like before Chavez became president.

> NB: shanty towns can be described as settlements of poor people who live in dwellings made from scrap materials – often plywood, corrugated metal, and sheets of plastic.

For example:

- few doctors and many unable to pay for one if they could find one
- illnesses left untreated
- lots of people could not read
- parents not sending their children to school because they could not afford school meals or books
- poor housing – crowded and shabby
- no electricity or clean water
- people trying to make money by selling things on the street for very little money
- old and sick people with no means of getting money.

Key points:

- Chavez is one example of a president prioritising the needs of all of his/her people. Once in power, he could have chosen to keep his country's wealth for the rich.
- Chavez's policies have improved the lives of millions of people in Venezuela.
- Chavez does have opposition. Some of the wealthy people in Venezuela are racist towards him (because he is not of European descent, was not educated in the developed world and lived in poverty as a child) and most of the Venezuelan media write anti-Chavez stories about him not being civilised enough to run a country. Often stories about Chavez that go out to the rest of the world are influenced by this media.
- Venezuela is a wealthy country because of the oil it sells. Some countries do not have this amount of wealth and even with the **political will** (i.e. governments dedicated to addressing poverty) to do so, they could not sort out their country's poverty alone.

- The actions of Chavez had no impact on the country's wealthiest people. They remained rich.
- Many people also agree that to improve the plight of the world's poor, political leaders need strong will and determination to do so.

ACTIVITY 8

Type of activity
Poster production

Resources:
Pupil activity sheet 16 'Something we can do: buy **Fairtrade**' (p58); one per pair

Learning objective:
to consider Fairtrade, its impact and its relationship to the consumer, and to write a persuasive text.

Something we can do: buy Fairtrade

What to do:

1 Ask pupils if they have heard of the term 'Fairtrade' and if so, what have they heard? You could list their comments and refer to these during the activity.

2 Give pairs of pupils a copy of the sheet 'Something we can do: buy Fairtrade' (p58) which outlines the basics of what Fairtrade is and does. Read the text and ask pupils to consider the benefits of Fairtrade – as outlined on the sheet. Discuss the obvious benefits of Fairtrade – how it reduces **exploitation** and means that workers in developing countries are treated fairly and have a better standard of living than those people that farm or make produce that is not Fairtrade.

NB: there are several websites that explore the issues of Fairtrade – including its benefits. For example: http://www.fairtrade.org.uk/ and http://www.co-operative.coop/food/ethics/Ethical-trading/Fairtrade/

3 Ask pupils what they think might prevent all products from being Fairtrade. Their answers may include:

- Not all products come from places where people are poorly paid or treated unfairly so Fairtrade and its regulations are not necessary.
- Some Fairtrade products are slightly more expensive than non-Fairtrade products. This will put off some consumers so fewer Fairtrade products are sold and therefore fewer are likely be bought by shops.
- Fairtrade can mean that both the shops and the companies that package and transport a product make slightly less profit.
- Not everyone cares about the rights of the people that grow or make products.
- Many people like shopping to be convenient (near, easy, cheap) and if their nearest shop does not stock Fairtrade goods, they are less likely to buy them.

4 Ask pupils why some people might always try to buy Fairtrade products. Answers might include:

- They care about the rights of farmers and workers in the developing world.
- They can afford to or are prepared to spend a little more on food to protect the rights of workers in the developing world.
- They know about the benefits of buying Fairtrade.

5 Explain to pupils that, in pairs, they are going to design and draw a poster that would persuade someone to consider buying Fairtrade goods. Give pairs of pupils time to discuss a few ideas and then time to settle on the idea they believe will be the most persuasive. You could stipulate that posters:

- are not allowed simply to say, 'Buy Fairtrade'
- must include an image that is as persuasive as the text
- must include at least one fact about Fairtrade.

Key points:

- Fairtrade is a social movement that has developed to ensure that the people that grow or make certain products are paid and treated fairly.
- For people to commit to buying Fairtrade goods, they need to understand the benefits and be concerned for the lives of people they do not know.
- If people are unaware of the difference buying Fairtrade can make to people's lives, they are unlikely to even consider buying Fairtrade products.

Support/extension:

- Help pupils that struggle to think of ideas for their poster by discussing the following suggestions:
  1 Show a Fairtrade product and a happy worker behind it thanking the purchaser.
  2 Give a message that buying Fairtrade means you care.
  3 A poster that clearly shows what the Fairtrade logo means.
  4 A poster that informs you about the kind of products that can be Fairtrade and persuades people to stop and think about the choice of Fairtrade or non-Fairtrade before they buy one of these products.
- Pupils can investigate and list the Fairtrade goods they can find next time they are in a food shop or supermarket. They could also compare the prices of Fairtrade and non-Fairtrade goods.

ACTIVITY 9

Type of activity
Prioritising activity
Resources:
Pupil activity sheet 17 'What would we want?' (p59); one per pair
Learning objective:
to revisit the key issues relating to global poverty and consider what would need to happen if there was the **political will** to drive it!

What would we want?

What to do:

1 Tell pupils that they are about to be put in charge of the world.

2 Give pairs of pupils a copy of the sheet 'What would we want?' (p59). Read through the suggestions and ask pairs of pupils to cut out the cards.

3 Explain that all of the suggestions listed on the cards are worthwhile, but that the pupils' task is to decide in which order they think the ideas need to be done. The value in this activity is the discussions it prompts; therefore pupils should complete the task in pairs.

4 When pairs have put the ideas in order, match up two pairs of pupils to make a group of four and ask them to explain their order to each other. Next ask each group of four to agree upon a final order.

5 Once the group of four has its order, ask pupils to stick it onto a large sheet of paper. They should then draw pictures and write comments around the actions to explain why they believe each is important. Also ask each group to agree on a way of completing the following sentence: The most important thing to do if I were in charge of the world would be..

6 Depending upon time, ask each group to share their sentence and/or sheet to the rest of the class, explaining the decisions they made and why they made them.

7 Provide more information for consideration in response to pupils' feedback using the table below.

Suggestion	Key notes
Make sure all children – throughout the world – have a much better chance of reaching adulthood	Millions of children worldwide do not make it into adulthood through malnutrition or illness. In choosing to address childhood survival, many health, wellbeing and safety issues for children would have to be considered.

Make sure pregnant women worldwide are in good health	Many women worldwide die in childbirth because of poor health and poor healthcare. A healthy mother is more likely to survive childbirth and give birth to a healthy baby.
Make the developed world waste less resources	Some people would argue that huge consumption by the developed world drives the **exploitation** and poor treatment of the developing world. They also argue that the developed world 'takes more than its fair share of resources' and wastes materials that the developing world could use.
Get rid of extreme hunger and make sure everyone has enough to eat	There is enough water and food to support the world population but the world's decision makers would need to commit to this for it to happen.
Ensure everyone has clean drinking water	
Make sure that everyone has a clean and safe home	People can survive without a clean and safe home but their existence is likely to be very vulnerable to poverty, hunger, poor physical and mental health, unemployment, etc.
Make sure the environment is protected	Damaging the environment has a variety of consequences including: Ruining land so it becomes unsuitable for farming. Fewer resources for those that survive by 'living off the land'. Climate change, which appears to mean an increase in natural disasters and other consequences that hit the world's most poor the hardest. This is likely to continue.
Make sure every child in the world gets education up to the age of 11	Education increases an individual's chance of not living in poverty. Education helps a nation to develop.
Make sure women get the same rights as men throughout the world	Worldwide, women suffer more from the ill-effects of poverty and are less likely to: have enough to eat (often giving up food so their children can eat), access education, get work, be exploited and mistreated, etc.

Key points:

- 'Make all countries work better together and agree and act upon what needs to happen worldwide' is often the first action needed as any one country working in isolation is unlikely to have enough impact on each of the suggestions. However, a handful of the world's wealthiest countries could make a significant difference if they were determined to do so.

Support/extension:

- Pupils can look at various anti-poverty websites to see the work they are prioritising.
- Pupils could write a list of things they believe everyone in the world has a right to.

Imagine this...

Imagine a room about the size of a classroom with 30 people in it (about the number of people in a class). One quarter of the room has plenty of furniture (including a plush sofa), a carpet, toys, books, games, a computer and a television. This quarter is very comfortable, warm, nicely decorated with pictures on the wall. The rest of the room, however, is shabby and draughty and has nothing in it except a few bowls and cups.

In the comfortable corner there are four people sitting at a table eating a huge roast dinner. They are drinking water with their meal. They got the water from a tap in the kitchen area of their corner of the room. They have a pudding too and all agree it's probably too much to eat. In fact, they don't manage to eat it all and end up scraping a fair amount into the bin. Everyone at the table looks healthy and happy. They are sitting and chatting about what they are going to watch on television, which books they like reading and which games they might play.

Everyone else is watching them from the shabby part of the room. They have not eaten since yesterday and will be lucky if they find some food at all today. They are drinking water, but they could not use the tap in the room. They had to bring their water from a well about half a mile away using a heavy container. The water is cloudy. Everyone looks extremely thin and several of the children look really ill. People are sitting on the ground and look as if they are suffering.

1) In what ways is this room not realistic?
2) How do you think the people eating the roast dinner would feel if they looked at the other people in the room?
3) What do you think the other people in the room are thinking and feeling as they watch the four people in the comfortable part of the room?
4) If these people were really in a room together, how do you think they would behave?

What causes global poverty?

There is no single cause for worldwide poverty.

Here are some of the many causes of global poverty. For each of these causes circle the things you think they could affect.

Cause of poverty	What this could affect				
Fuel and food prices going up	having enough food to eat	ability to earn money	education	health	shelter
Soil being overused and no longer good for growing crops	having enough food to eat	ability to earn money	education	health	shelter
Wealthy governments encouraging farmers to grow biofuels to sell to other countries rather than food for local people	having enough food to eat	ability to earn money	education	health	shelter
Diseases like AIDS and malaria that can kill	having enough food to eat	ability to earn money	education	health	shelter
Natural disasters – floods, hurricanes	having enough food to eat	ability to earn money	education	health	shelter
Conflict and war	having enough food to eat	ability to earn money	education	health	shelter
Lack of education	having enough food to eat	ability to earn money	education	health	shelter
No clean water supply	having enough food to eat	ability to earn money	education	health	shelter
Corrupt governments that do not care about the people in their country	having enough food to eat	ability to earn money	education	health	shelter
Children unable to attend school because they need to work to provide much needed money for their family	having enough food to eat	ability to earn money	education	health	shelter
Climate change	having enough food to eat	ability to earn money	education	health	shelter
A country being in debt and having to pay interest	having enough food to eat	ability to earn money	education	health	shelter

Consider the life of a street child in India

1) Which of the following comments do you think a street child in India is likely to have made?

> I survive by eating food that restaurants sometimes throw away.

> I cannot go home because I stole money from my dad.

> I sleep in a nice warm bed every night.

> I sometimes don't get enough to eat.

> I am good at begging because I am so small.

> Everyone always makes us feel welcome.

2) Use the text to try and make up some more comments you think a street child in India could have made about their life.

3) Make a list of things you have that you think a street child does not have. Try to make your list as long as possible.

A freeze-frame

In pairs, produce a freeze-frame showing one part of a street child's life. You might choose to show one of the following:

- a child being chased away by someone
- a child begging
- a child trying to find a place to sleep
- a child trying to get food

When you are in your freeze-frame, try to imagine what you would be thinking and feeling, and what your facial expression might be.

What does poverty look like on the African continent?

Everjoice Makuve supports an organisation called Widows and Orphans Relief and Development Trust International which works mostly on the African continent and aims to reduce poverty by helping people to help themselves.

Everjoice shared some information about different aspects of poverty in some of the fifteen African countries her organisation works to support.

Rich and poor

"Like in many countries throughout the world, every country I work with has wealthy people and those living in extreme poverty. Wealthy people can have a perfectly comfortable life in African countries."

Water

"Clean water is available in some of the places I have visited. People go to the bore hole and queue for it."

Education

"Many children living in poverty, despite their lack of food, wish more than anything to go to school. This is because they see school as a means of getting a better life. However, school is not a choice for many children. A five-year-old girl in Liberia once approached me and asked me to pay for her school fees – it was what she wanted more than anything. If parents have to choose between sending their child to school or feeding him/her, of course they will choose food. Sending a child to school costs money in African countries and not every place has a school. Some schools are very poorly equipped. I saw a school in the capital city of Malawi where only the teacher had a chair and table and the pupils had to sit on the floor."

Food

"Children living in poverty often survive on one meal a day – paid for by their parents or well-wishers in the case of child-headed families. In Liberia this meal would typically be fish, beef, rice, sweet potato leaves and other vegetables grown nearby. Children that live on the streets won't be guaranteed any food and have to survive by scrounging."

Helping people to help themselves

"There is a tendency to overlook the resourcefulness of people just because they are living in poverty. My organisation understands that with a little guidance most communities can work together to help themselves. We strongly believe that coming out of poverty is about building people's capacity to problem solve.

Healthcare

"Child mortality is much higher than in the developed world. Children can die of malnutrition or preventable diseases like measles. Healthcare, if it is available, costs money."

SHEET 16 — Something we can do: buy Fairtrade

® When someone buys something that carries the FAIRTRADE Mark (for example: coffee, cocoa, sugar, tea, bananas), they know the people that grew the crop have been paid fairly and have received additional money to invest in their communities. This is because Fairtrade organisations ensure that farmers in developing countries growing crops are treated fairly and paid a proper wage for their work. They also decide how to invest in their communities, for example, building schools and hospitals. If this has happened, then the food's packaging can have the FAIRTRADE Mark printed onto it.

Fairtrade has meant that many people worldwide have had their living conditions improved.

> With Fairtrade income we have made improvements in our community. Before we slept on the ground and did not have basic amenities. Now some of us have floors, some furniture, sanitary services and potable water. If we sold all of our production at Fairtrade prices, our dreams would come true.
> Alexa Marin Colindres, member PRODECOOP Coffee Cooperative, Nicaragua
> From www.transfairusa.org

Fairtrade means:

- Farmers and workers in the developing world can support their families
- Farmers grow their crops in a way that looks after the environment and that means the land does not get over-farmed and can keep producing crops
- Farmers can invest in their communities, for example building schools, hospitals and providing clean water
- Children can go to school because their parents earn enough so that the children do not need to work in the fields too.

What would we want?

If you were put in charge of the world tomorrow, what would be your priorities? Put the ideas below in order: from the things that you think need to happen first, to those that can happen last.

Make sure all children – throughout the world – have a much better chance of reaching adulthood	Get rid of extreme hunger and make sure everyone has enough to eat	Make sure pregnant women worldwide are in good health
Make sure the environment is protected	Ensure everyone has clean drinking water	Make the developed world waste less resources
Make sure every child in the world gets education up to the age of 11	Make sure that everyone has a clean and safe home	Make sure women get the same rights as men throughout the world
Make all countries work better together and agree and act upon what needs to happen worldwide	Reduce worldwide deaths from diseases like AIDS, dysentery and malaria	Stop the mistreatment of people (including children) through poor working conditions

Assembly Ideas

This section outlines assemblies that could be delivered using the activities in this book.

Assembly 1

Learning objective

- to consider material wealth and how important it is or is not.

Key points

- Being rich does not automatically lead to contentment.
- The things that lead to true happiness are often free.

Activities

1 Ask the assembly hall, 'If you were given one wish, what would it be?' (with a ban on more wishes of course). Take a few answers and make a note of those that would wish to be rich.

2 Ask a few pupils that said they would wish to be rich to stand at the front of the assembly hall and ask, 'Can anyone tell me why they would like to be rich?' Take a few suggestions – which will probably all be about material wealth – and then ask the pupils to sit down.

3 Next tell a story of a very rich man. He had many huge houses around the world, a helicopter, lots of cars, servants and just about anything money could buy. However, he was never satisfied and the more he got the more he wanted. This made him a pretty dissatisfied person and as he became richer, he had fewer and fewer friends. (You could have prepared a pupil particularly skilled in improvisation to play this character and introduce him to the assembly. Keep the character grumpy and greedy.)

4 Ask pupils, 'If this man could make one wish, what do you think he should wish for?'

After giving pupils some thinking time, take several answers.

5 Use pupils to count up different kinds of answers. For example, one pupil could keep tally of 'happiness' answers, another 'friends' etc. When you have collected several answers, ask pupils if you can have these things whether you are rich or not.

6 Finish the assembly by giving a message that says:

- Many people strive to be rich but if you are not happy without money, you are unlikely to be happy with it.
- Things that make a person truly happy rarely cost money.

You could also explore some of the following quotations:

> It is the heart that makes a man rich. He is rich according to what he is, not according to what he has.
> – Henry Ward Beecher

> It is not the man who has too little, but the man who craves more, that is poor.
> – Seneca

> Make no mistake, my friend, it takes more than money to make men rich.
> – A. P. Gouthey

> If you want to feel rich, just count all of the things you have that money can't buy.
> – Anonymous

Reflection

Ask pupils to imagine themselves really happy at a time when they are doing something that does not cost money.

Assembly 2

Learning objective

- to consider Maslow's hierarchy of needs and how worldwide disasters can affect individuals' quality of life.

Key points

- What is needed to survive?
- What do we need to live a fulfilling life?

Activities

1 Before the assembly make up some cards with the following words written on them:

- water
- food
- sleep
- health
- safety
- family
- friends
- respect
- confidence
- achievements

2 Hand out the cards to ten pupils and ask them to hold their cards so that the assembly can read them.

3 Explain to pupils that the cards are going to be sorted from the things we need most of all to those we need less. Ask pupils which three things are needed to survive as human beings and take their answers (food, water and sleep). Ask the three pupils holding those cards to stand at one end of the imaginary spectrum.

4 Then ask pupils to consider what we most need next, and so on, until you get a 'spectrum' something like the bullet pointed list above.

5 Go through the list from most needed to least needed, giving examples (humorous if possible) and explanations about how you know you have each thing.

6 Next, explain to pupils how it would be difficult to fulfil the three 'higher' needs if you didn't have the basic ones. For example, if you did not feel safe, it would be hard to achieve things. It would also be hard to do things like learn, be creative, etc)

7 Ask pupils to consider a country:

- at war
- in famine
- after a natural disaster like a hurricane.

Which of these the ten needs listed above do they believe would be affected for individuals in such a country? (potentially all of them).

8 Finish by considering how lucky we are in the UK that many of us do not have to experience a daily struggle for our basic needs like many people worldwide have to.

Reflection

Ask pupils to think of three things they are really grateful for.

Assembly 3

Learning objective

- to consider how the media presents success and how this might make us feel.

Key points

- How does the media portray people?
- What does success look like in adverts?
- What could be an alternative view of success?

Activities

1 Before the assembly, ask a mixed-sex group of pupils to prepare to be people as they are portrayed in TV adverts. To do this suggest they make up a typical:

- car advert
- perfume or makeup advert and/or
- overseas holiday advert.

Encourage pupils to put the following into their adverts:

- confident, happy looking people
- being perfect
- references to beauty and looking young

- references to owning lots of things and living in big houses etc.

2 Ask these pupils to show the assembly hall their adverts.

3 Ask pupils to imagine that they were aliens and these adverts were the only source of information they had about Earth. What would they think the people on this planet were all like? Take some suggestions.

4 Ask pupils if they think everyone is like the people from such adverts. Also ask them in what way these adverts are unrealistic, e.g. not everyone is wealthy, young, always happy and healthy. Explain that these images can make people feel like their lives are not as they should be and that this can cause people to feel dissatisfied.

5 Ask pupils to consider how these adverts show success. For example, the people in these adverts are:

- young
- attractive to most people
- well dressed at all times
- rich and own many things
- live in big houses
- powerful
- always happy
- live an exciting life full of action.

6 Ask pupils to think of alternative ways people can be successful that are more realistic and not based on an expensive lifestyle that most people do not have. For example:

- being a nice person to know and having friends
- always looking on the bright side – being an optimist
- coping well when things go wrong
- always trying hard and not giving up easily
- liking ourselves as we are – with strengths and weaknesses
- getting good at something
- being confident.

7 If time allows, pupils could show a pre-prepared TV advert selling this second kind of success.

Reflection

Ask pupils to picture themselves as really successful. Get them to reflect on what they might have done or what might have happened to make them this way.

Assembly 4

Learning objective

• to consider aspirations.

Key points

• What are aspirations?
• What helps people to fulfil their potential?

Activities

1 Explain what aspirations are: hopes and dreams for our future. An example of an aspiration is that someone might want to become a doctor or a nurse. Other people might not have aspirations. Ask the assembly if anyone has any aspirations and ask willing volunteers to share. You could share any aspirations you had or have.

2 Ask pupils to imagine that they were being given advice about their future and read out a selection of the following quotations. After each one is read, ask pupils what they think each piece of advice is saying.

The road to success is lined with many tempting parking spaces.
– Traditional Proverb

You can make goals for family, relationships, anything.
– Michael Johnson

Success usually comes to those who are too busy to be looking for it.
– Henry David Thoreau

Attitude determines altitude.
– Anonymous

To succeed.. you need to find something to hold on to, something to motivate you, something to inspire you.
– Tony Dorsett

A big shot is a little shot that kept shooting.
– Anonymous

Nobody made a greater mistake than he who did nothing because he could do only a little.
– Edmund Burke

Life is a great big canvas, and you should throw all the paint you can on it.
– Danny Kaye

If your ship doesn't come in, swim out to it.
– Jonathan Winters

Never giving up and pushing forward will unlock all the potential we are capable of.
– Christy Borgeld

Some make it happen, some watch it happen, and some say, "What happened?"
– Anonymous

What we see depends mainly on what we look for.
– John Lubbock

Obstacles are those frightful things you see when you take your eyes off your goals.
– Anonymous

Anyone who thinks the sky is the limit, has limited imagination.
– Anonymous

3 Ask pupils why they think having aspirations might be important. Example answers may include:

• You know what you're aiming for.
• You can be more determined if you have a clear aspiration and know what you need to do to get there.
• Aspirations can help you aim to do something worthwhile with your life.
• Aspirations can help prevent a person from living in poverty.

4 Ask pupils what they think could stop a person from reaching their aspirations. Example answers may include:

• not having any aspirations
• lack of determination
• not knowing the choices there are
• apathy
• assuming they have to do the same as their parents/carers did

Reflection

Ask pupils to think about their hopes and dreams for their futures.

Assembly 5

Learning objective

- to consider inequality.

Key points

- What is global inequality?
- Why is the solution to global inequality not as simple as handing over money or food to people living in poverty?

Activities

1 Read the description of a room on Pupil activity sheet 12 'Imagine this...' (p54); or, if time allows, ask some pupils to re-create the scene portrayed in this text in front of the assembly.

2 Ask pupils to consider the questions at the bottom of the sheet.

3 Use the teachers' notes on page 42 to explore the metaphor further with pupils.

3 Ask pupils to consider things that they waste (e.g. food, belongings we throw out just because we don't want them any more, etc). Ask pupils to consider how people living in absolute poverty might feel if they knew about the way we wasted things. Highlight that even though we cannot just hand over our food and possessions to people living in poverty around the world (and they might not actually be able to make use of them), it's good to be reminded that we do take so much for granted that other people simply cannot.

Reflection

Ask pupils to think of three things they take for granted that some people worldwide cannot assume they will always have.

Glossary

aspirations — a strong desire to achieve something e.g. qualifications or a particular job

basic human needs — the minimum resources needed for long-term well-being

credit card — a card issued by banks allowing the holder to pay for goods and services on credit or with borrowed money

debt — something that is owed, such as money, to someone or something else

empathy — being able to understand or imagine how it might feel to be somebody else

exploitation — to take unfair advantage of a person or situation because it benefits you

global poverty — the lack of basic human needs in certain areas of the world, due to the inability to afford them

government — a body, or group, who make decisions about how a certain community or area should be ruled

inequality — an unequal distribution of money or resources

interest — a charge for the use of credit or borrowed money

poverty — the lack of human needs, due to the inability to afford them

sanitation — the use of practical measures for the preservation of health

shanty town — a section of a town or city where very poor people live in huts or similar shelters

stereotype — a belief about or conception of a particular group of people

stigma — a mark of disgrace

subsidised — to be supported by financial aid from another person or group

success — the attainment of something that is considered positive, e.g. wealth, fame

sympathy — being able to feel sorry for somebody or to understand how they feel

tax — a compulsory payment or contribution to the government of the country you live in, based on how much you earn or own

welfare — health and well-being